101 Latin Hits for

Piano/Organ edition with guitar

Wise Publications
London / New York / Sydney

Exclusive Distributors:
Music Sales Limited
8/9 Frith Street, London W1V 5TZ, England.
Music Sales Pty Limited
120 Rothschild Avenue, Rosebery, NSW 2018, Australia.

This book © Copyright 1992 by Wise Publications.
Order No. AM84724
ISBN 0-7119-2644-1

Design & art direction by Michael Bell Design.
Cover illustration by Hilary McManus.
Compiled by Peter Evans & Peter Lavender.
Music processed by Hillmob Music Services & MSS Studios.

Music Sales' complete catalogue lists thousands of
titles and is free from your local music shop, or direct
from Music Sales Limited.Please send a cheque/postal
order for £1.50 for postage to: Music Sales Limited,
Newmarket Road, Bury St. Edmunds, Suffolk IP33 3YB.

Your Guarantee of Quality:

**As publishers, we strive to produce every book
to the highest commercial standards.**

**The book has been carefully designed to minimise
awkward page turns and to make playing from it
a real pleasure.**

**Particular care has been given to specifying
acid-free, neutral-sized paper which has not been
chlorine bleached but produced with special
regard for the environment.**

**Throughout, the printing and binding have been
planned to ensure a sturdy, attractive publication
which should give years of enjoyment.**

**If your copy fails to meet our high standards,
please inform us and we will gladly replace it.**

Printed in the United Kingdom by
Scotprint Limited, Musselburgh, Edinburgh.

Classified Rhythm Index:

Arranger's Note:

For the purposes of this collection, the rhythms have been selected for modern dance accompaniment rather than for the original forms associated with the more traditional melodies.

In certain cases, suggested rhythms can be substituted with more simple (or more exotic) styles. For example: Beguine - Mambo or Rhumba; Bossa Nova - Samba, etc. You should adjust your tempo accordingly.

1
Amapola

Words by Albert Gamse.
Music by Joseph M. Lacalle.

2
Adios

English Words by Eddie Woods.
Music & Spanish Words by Enric Madriguera.

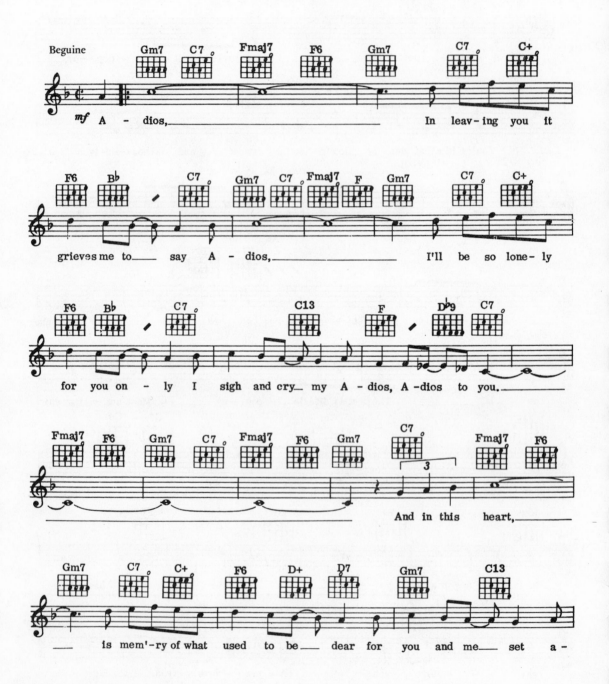

A - dios,_____ In leav-ing you it grieves me to___ say A - dios,_____ I'll be so lone-ly for you on - ly I sigh and cry__ my A - dios, A - dios to you.___ And in this heart,___ is mem'-ry of what used to be___ dear for you and me___ set a-

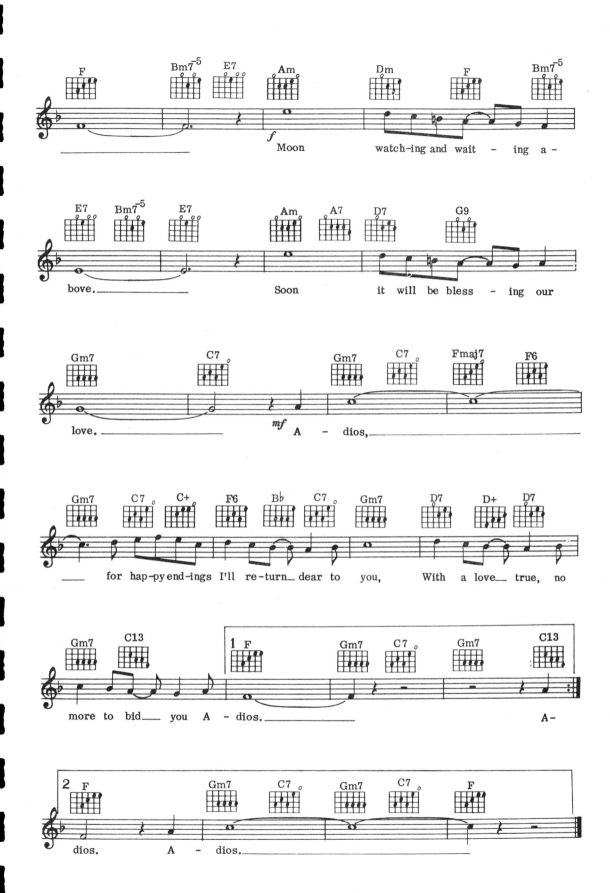

3
A Man Without Love
(Quando M'innamoro)

Music and Original Lyrics by R. Livraghi, M. Panzeri & D. Pace.
English Lyrics by Barry Mason.

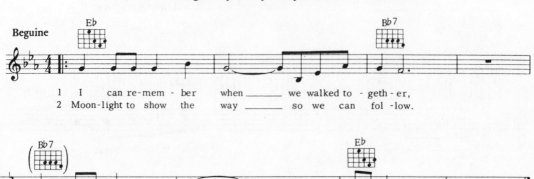

Beguine

1 I can re-mem - ber when ____ we walked to - geth - er,
2 Moon-light to show the way ____ so we can fol -low.

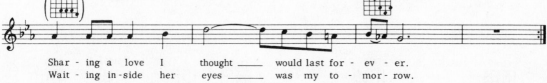

Shar - ing a love I thought ____ would last for - ev - er.
Wait - ing in -side her eyes ____ was my to - mor - row.

Then some-thing changed her mind, ____ her kiss-es told me.

tacet

I had no lov - ing arms ____ to hold me.

Ev'-ry day I wake up, then I start to break up, Lone-ly is a man with-out love. __
Know-ing that it's cloud-y a - bove. __

Ev'-ry day I start out, then I cry my heart out. Lone-ly is a man with-out love. __

I can-not face this world ___ that's fal-len down on me. So, if you see my

girl, ___ please send her home to me. Tell her a-bout my heart ___ that's slow-ly

dy-ing. Say, I can't stop my-self ___ from cry-ing.

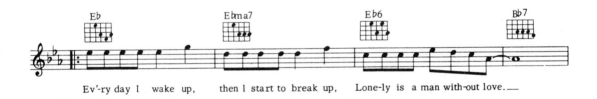

Ev'-ry day I wake up, then I start to break up, Lone-ly is a man with-out love. ___

Ev'-ry day I start out, then I cry my heart out, Lone-ly is a man without love. ___

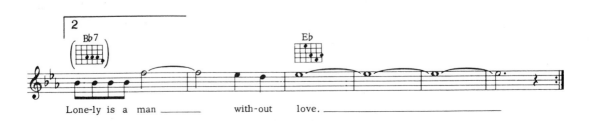

Lone-ly is a man ___ with-out love. ___

4
Americano

Music by Xavier Cugat & George Rosner.
Words by Tom Smith.

Beguine

South - ern breeze, _____ soft and gent - ly ca - ress - ing, _____

_____ To you, now I am con - fess - ing, _____ In my heart there is a

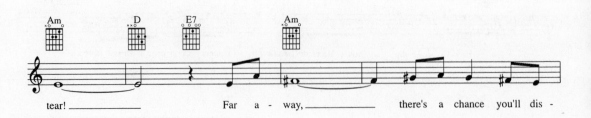

tear! _____ Far a - way, _____ there's a chance you'll dis -

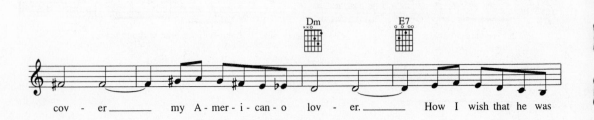

cov - er _____ my A - mer - i - can - o lov - er. _____ How I wish that he was

here! _____ His kiss made _____ ev - 'ry night so ex - cit - ing, _____

_ What good now, _____ Are the stars up a - bove? _____ South - ern

breeze, _____ Blow a kiss thru the air for _____ While I say a lit - tle

prayer for _____ my A - mer - i - can - o love! _____

5
Amor

Spanish Words by Ricardo Lopez Mendez.
English Words by Sunny Skylar. Music by Gabriel Ruiz.

Beguine

A - mor,   A - mor,   A - mor,
A - mor,   a - mor,   a - mor

This word so sweet   that I re - peat,   Means I a - dore you.
Na - cio de ti,   Na - cio de mi,   de la es - pe - ran - za

A - mor,   A - mor,   My love,
A - mor,   a - mor,   a - mor,

Would you den - y   this heart that I   have placed be - fore you.
Na - cio de Dios   pa ra los dos,   Na - cio del al ma.

I can't find a - no - ther word with mean - ing so clear,   My lips try to whis - per swee - ter
Sen tir que tus be - sos a - ni - da - ron en mi,   I - gual que pa - lo - mas men - sa -

6
Amorita
(Fue Mentira)

Words & Music by Carlos Barberena.
English Lyrics by Len Lawson.

7
Arrivederci Roma

Words by Garinei & Giovannini.
English Lyric by Carl Sigman. Music by Renato Rascel.

Ar - ri - ve - der - ci Ro - ma, _____ Good - bye, Good - bye to Rome. _____ Ci - ty of a mil - lion moon - lit pla - ces, Ci - ty of a mil - lion warm em - bra - ces, Where I found the one of all the fa - ces, Far from

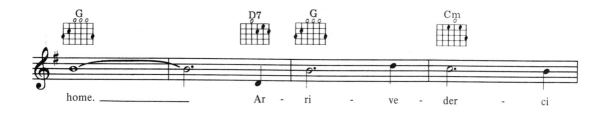

home. _____ Ar - ri - ve - der - ci

Ro - ma, _____ It's time for us to

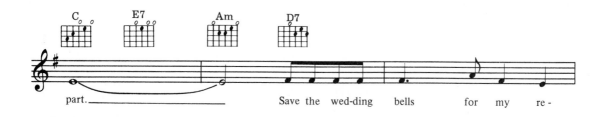

part. _____ Save the wed-ding bells for my re -

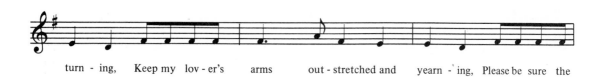

turn - ing, Keep my lov - er's arms out - stretched and yearn - ing, Please be sure the

flame of love keeps burn - ing in her heart. _____

8
Be Mine Tonight
(Noche De Ronda)

English Lyric by Sunny Skylar.
Music by Maria Teresa Lara.

See the set - ting sun, the ev'-ning's just be-gun and love is in the

air; _____ Be mine to - night. _____

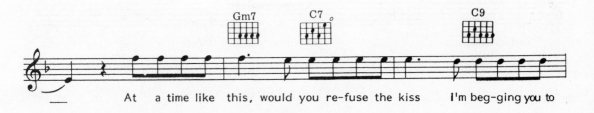

_____ At a time like this, would you re-fuse the kiss I'm beg-ging you to

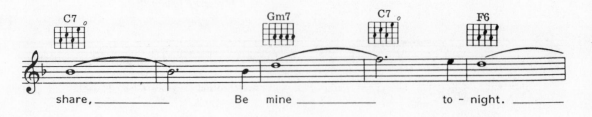

share, _____ Be mine _____ to - night. _____

Pro - mise this my own, be-fore the night has flown, you'll tell me that you

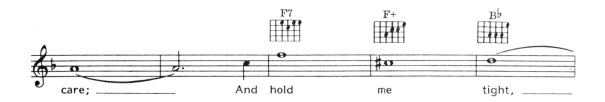

care; _____ And hold me tight, _____

__ Whis - per love words, _____ oh, so ten - der. _____ Give your

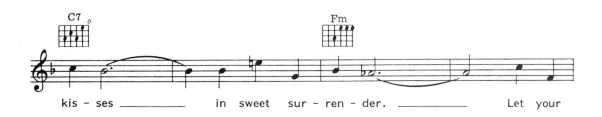

kis - ses _____ in sweet sur - ren - der. _____ Let your

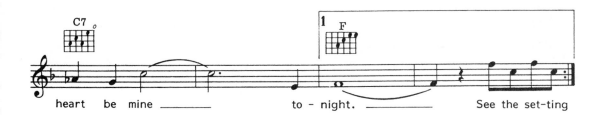

heart be mine _____ to - night. _____ See the set - ting

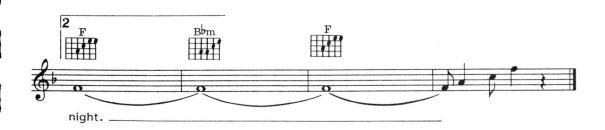

night. _____

9
Come Closer To Me
(Acercate Mas)

English Lyric by Al Stewart.
Music by Osvaldo Farres.

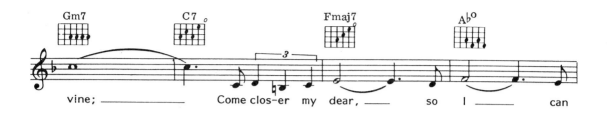

vine; _____ Come clos-er my dear, _____ so I _____ can

hear mus-ic in my heart; I've wait-ed so long _____ to

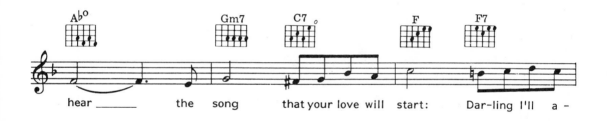

hear _____ the song that your love will start: Dar-ling I'll a-

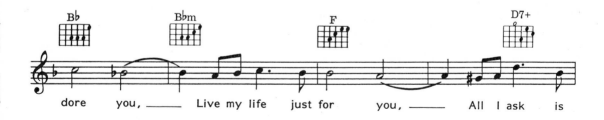

dore you, _____ Live my life just for you, _____ All I ask is

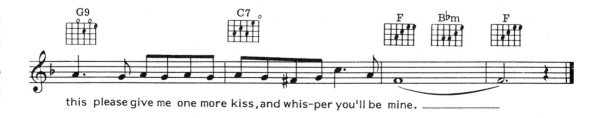

this please give me one more kiss, and whis-per you'll be mine. _____

10
Green Eyes

Words by L. Wolfe Gilbert & Reg Connelly.
Music by Nilo Menendez.

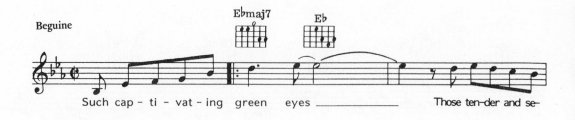

Such cap - ti - vat - ing green eyes _____ Those ten-der and se-

rene eyes _____ Those fas-cin-a-ting Green Eyes _____ They're lov-ing and they're

true _____ The sea be-neath the blue skies _____ is en-vy-ing your

green eyes_____ The beau-ty of the wood - land _____ keeps re-mind-ing me

too. _____ My heart where-in my love lies _____ Is tell-ing me of

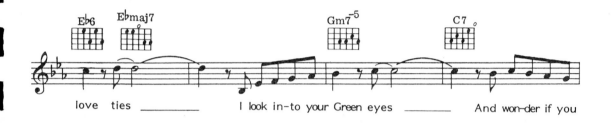

love ties _____ I look in-to your Green eyes _____ And won-der if you

care _____ My dreams are all a-bout you _____ I'll nev-er nev-er

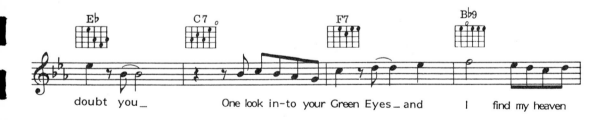

doubt you_ One look in-to your Green Eyes_and I find my heaven

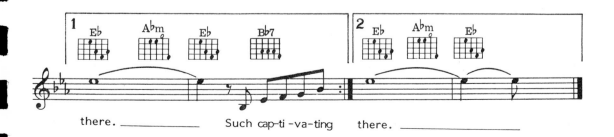

there. _____ Such cap-ti -va-ting there. _____

11
History Of Love
(Historia De Un Amor)

English Lyric by Dorothy Dodd.
Music by Carlos Almaran.

Beguine

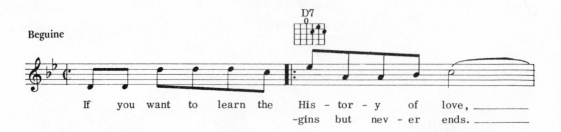

If you want to learn the His - tor - y of love, _____
-gins but nev - er ends. _____

_____ First you have to solve the mys - t'ry that is love. _____ Its en-chant-ment, its temp-
_____ And if on - ly we were slight - ly clos - er friends, _____ We could stud - y it to-

-ta - tion, And the kind of fasc - in - a - tion that is mine when I'm with
-geth - er, And per-haps dis - cov - er

you. _____ Love's a stor - y that be - wheth-er, All it says is real-ly

true! Love's a feel-ing that we don't ev - er quite un - der-

12
In Old Lisbon
(Lisboa Antigua)

Music by Paul Portela, J. Galhardo & A. do Vale.
English Lyric by Henry Dupree.

13
It's Now Or Never

Words & Music by G. Capurro & E. Di Capua.
English Lyric by Aaron Schroeder & Wally Gold.

To Interlude   3.   Bb13   Eb   Ab   Eb   Fine

(opt. octave lower- - - - - - -)

____ 1. When I first ___ my love won't wait. _____
Just like a

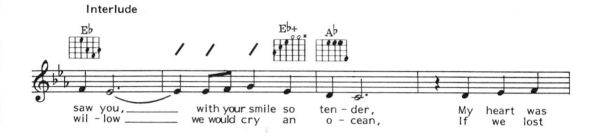

Interlude

Eb   Eb+   Ab

saw you, _____ with your smile so ten - der,   My heart was
wil - low _____ we would cry an o - cean,   If we lost

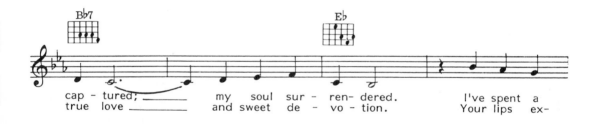

Bb7   Eb

cap - tured; _____ my soul sur - ren - dered.   I've spent a
true love _____ and sweet de - vo - tion.   Your lips ex-

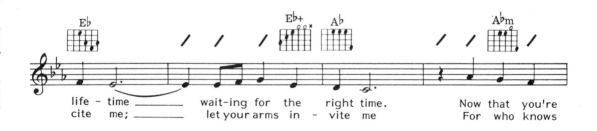

Eb   Eb+   Ab   Abm

life - time _____ wait-ing for the right time.   Now that you're
cite me; _____ let your arms in - vite me   For who knows

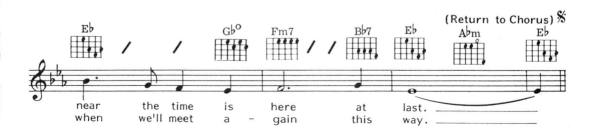

(Return to Chorus) 𝄋

Eb   Gbo   Fm7   Bb7   Eb   Abm   Eb

near the time is here at last. _____
when we'll meet a - gain this way. _____

14
La Golondrina
(When I'm Alone)

Music by N. Serradell.
English Lyric by Paco Liez.

Beguine

When I'm a - lone,_____ the mem'ries of you fill____ the emp - ty
- lone,_____ or in the warmth of some - one's ten - der

room, and in my nights_____ is sleep but not a dream.____
love, and do you sleep,_____ to wake with gen -tle smiles.____

___ You were the pearl I threw____ back in the sea____
I have no peace, just long - ing and re - gret____

___ I am the shell, that's all that's left of
for love I lost and nev - er can for -

1 me.____ Are you a - __ **2** Once you were here____ in my

arms, long - ing on - ly to please_____ me and yet my

gree - dy__ heart____ grew dis - con - tent so eas - i - ly____

15
Feelings
(Dime)

By Morris Albert & Louis Gaste.

16
La Paloma

Composed by S. Yradier.

Dm7 G7

Que se _____ vi - no tras de mí que sí se -
Nos i _____ re - mos a dor - mir a - llá voy
Y el cu _____ ra dos hi - so - pa - zos que sí se -

C

ñor _____
yo _____
ñor _____

Si a tu ven - ta - na lle - ga u - na pa -

G7

lo - ma _____ Trá - ta - la con ca - ri - ño que es mi per -

C

so - na _____ cuén - ta - le tus a - mo - res bien de mi

G7

vi - da _____ Có - ro - na - la de flo - res que es co - sa

mí - a   Ay! chi-ni-ta que sí   Ay! que da-me tu a -

mor ay!_____ Que ven-te con - mi-go chi-ni - ta a don-de vi-vo

yo   Ay! chi-ni-ta que sí   Ay! que da-me tu a -

mor   ay! _____ Que ven-te con - mi-go, chi-ni - ta

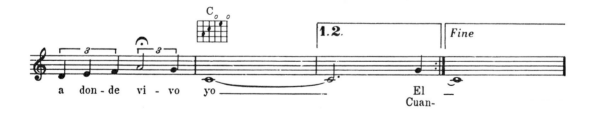

a don-de vi - vo yo _____ El
Cuan-

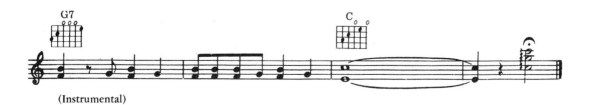

(Instrumental)

17
Mas Que Nada
(Say No More)

Words & Music by Jorge Ben.
English Lyric by Norman Gimbel.

18
Non Dimenticar

Music by P.G. Redi.
English Lyric by Shelley Dobbins. Original Italian Lyric by Michele Galdieri.

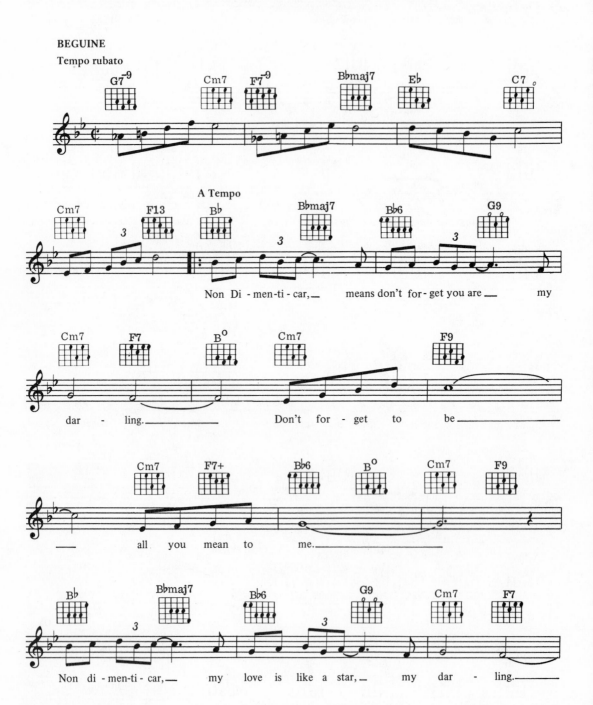

19
Petticoats Of Portugal
(Rapariga Do Portugal)

Words & Music by Michael Durso, Mel Mitchell & Murl Cahn.

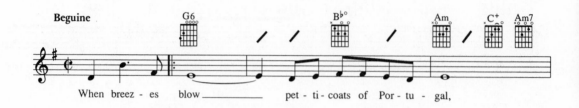

When breez - es blow _____ pet - ti - coats of Por - tu - gal,

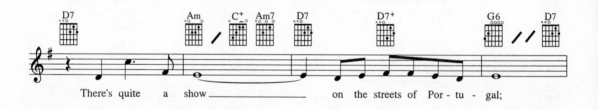

There's quite a show _____ on the streets of Por - tu - gal;

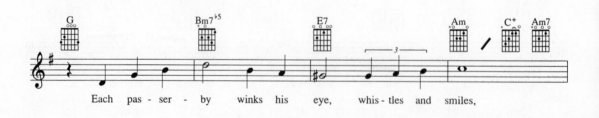

Each pas - ser - by winks his eye, whis - tles and smiles,

The ooh's and ah's, loud hur - rahs, ech - o for miles;

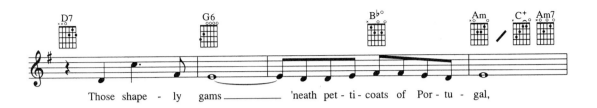

Those shape - ly gams _____ 'neath pet - ti - coats of Por - tu - gal,

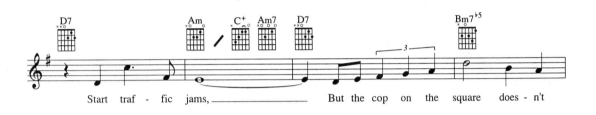

Start traf - fic jams, _____ But the cop on the square does - n't

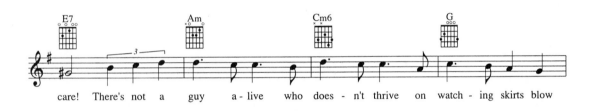

care! There's not a guy a - live who does - n't thrive on watch - ing skirts blow

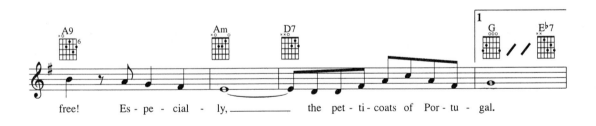

free! Es - pe - cial - ly, _____ the pet - ti - coats of Por - tu - gal.

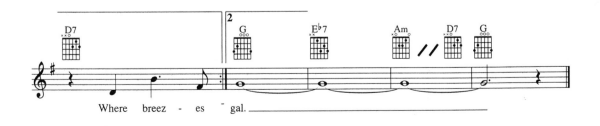

Where breez - es gal. _____

20
Magic Is The Moonlight

Music by Maria Grever.
English Words by Charles Pasquale.

21
Perfidia

English Lyric by Milton Leeds.
Music & Spanish Words by Alberto Dominguez.

22
Perhaps, Perhaps, Perhaps

English Words by Joe Davis.
Music by Osvaldo Farres.

23
Stars In Your Eyes
(Mar)

Music by Gabriel Ruiz.
Spanish Lyrics by R. Lopez Mendes. English Lyrics by Mort Green.

24
Summertime In Venice

Music by Icini.
English Words by Carl Sigman.

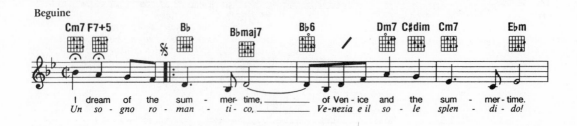

I dream of the sum - mer - time, _____ of Ven - ice and the sum - mer - time.
Un so - gno ro - man - ti - co, _____ Ve - nezia e il so - le splen - di - do!

I see the ca - fes, _____ the sun - lit days _____ with you, my
Do - vun - que sa - ro, _____ non li po - tro _____ di - men - ti -

love. The an - tique shop _____ where we'd stop _____
car! Di que - sta e - sta - te sul mar _____

_____ for a sou - ve - nir. _____ The
non po - tran mo - rir _____ in

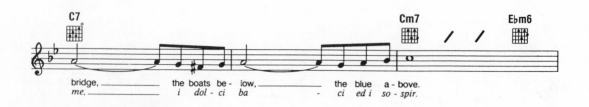

bridge, _____ the boats be - low, _____ the blue a - bove.
me, _____ i dol - ci ba - ci ed i so - spir.

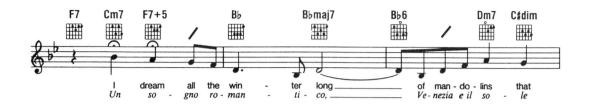

F7   Cm7   F7+5   Bb   Bbmaj7   Bb6   Dm7   C#dim

I   dream   all   the   win - ter   long_____ of   man-do-lins   that
Un   so - gno   ro-man - ti - co,_____ Ve - nezia e il   so - le

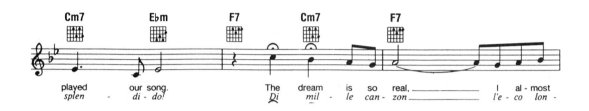

Cm7   Ebm   F7   Cm7   F7

played   our   song.   The   dream   is   so   real,_____ I   al - most
splen - di - do!   Di   mil - le   can - zon_____ l'e - co   lon -

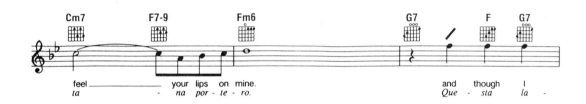

Cm7   F7-9   Fm6   G7   F   G7

feel_____ your   lips   on   mine.   and   though   I
ta - na   por - te - ro.   Que - sta   la -

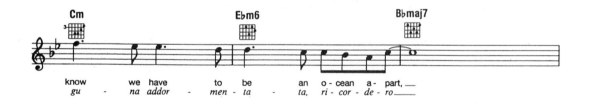

Cm   Ebm6   Bbmaj7

know   we   have   to   be   an   o - cean   a - part,___
gu - na   addor - men - ta - ta,   ri - cor - de - ro___

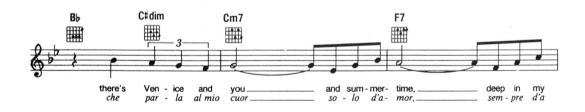

Bb   C#dim   Cm7   F7

there's   Ven - ice   and   you_____ and   sum-mer- time,_____ deep   in   my
che   par - la al mio   cuor_____ so - lo   d'a - mor,_____ sem - pre   d'a

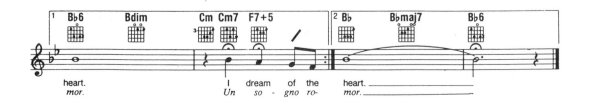

1. Bb6   Bdim   Cm   Cm7   F7+5   2. Bb   Bbmaj7   Bb6

heart.   I   dream   of   the   heart._____
mor.   Un   so - gno   ro-   mor.

25
Sway

Words by Norman Gimbel.
Music by Pablo Beltran Ruiz.

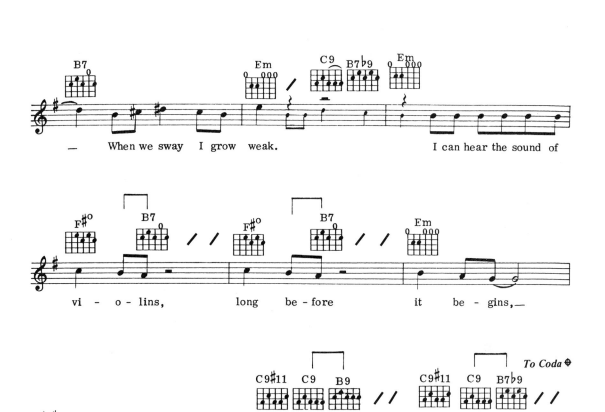

When we sway I grow weak. I can hear the sound of vi - o - lins, long be - fore it be - gins, __

Make me thrill as on - ly you know how, sway me smooth,

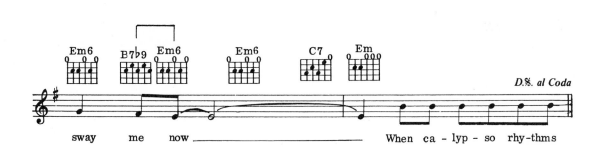

sway me now _____ When ca - lyp - so rhy-thms

To Coda ⊕

D.%. al Coda

⊕ *CODA*

sway me now. _ Sway me smooth, sway me now. _____

26
Spanish Eyes

Words by Charles Singleton, Eddie Snyder.
Music by Bert Kaempfert.

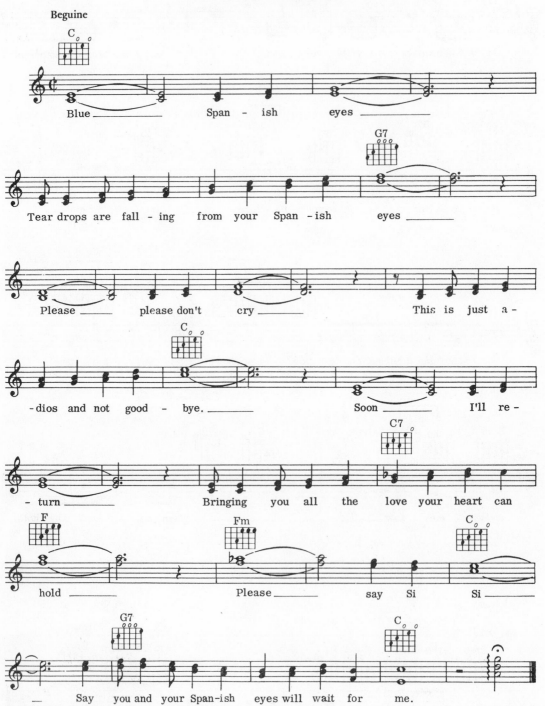

Blue ____ Span - ish eyes ____

Tear drops are fall - ing from your Span - ish eyes ____

Please ____ please don't cry ____ This is just a-

-dios and not good - bye. ____ Soon ____ I'll re-

-turn ____ Bringing you all the love your heart can

hold ____ Please ____ say Si Si

____ Say you and your Span - ish eyes will wait for me.

27
Tropical

Words & Music by Morton Gould.

28
Taboo

Words by S.K. Russell.
Spanish Words & Music by Margarita Lecuona.

29
Time Was
(Duerme)

English Lyric by S.K. Russell.
Music by Miguel Prado.

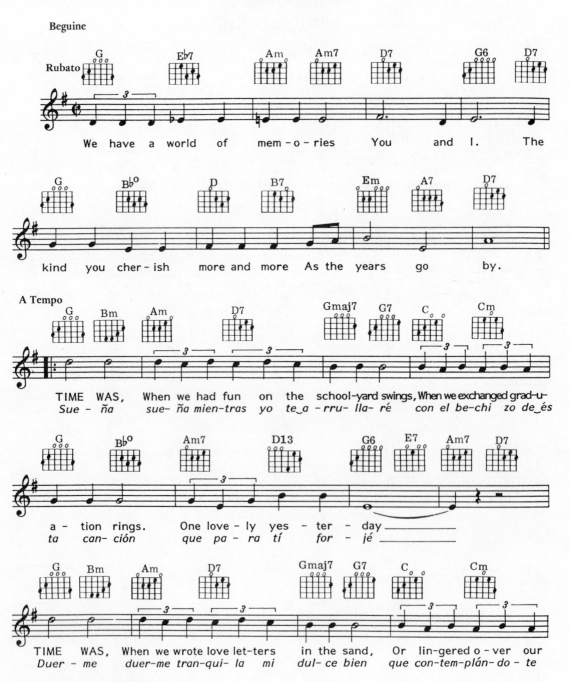

30
Without You
(Tres Palabras)

Music & Spanish Lyrics by Osvaldo Farres.
English Lyrics by Ray Gilbert.

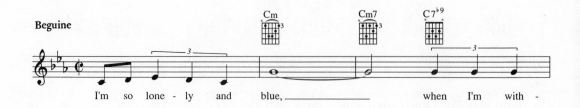

I'm so lone-ly and blue, _____ when I'm with-

out you, _____ I don't know what I'd do, _____ sweet-heart, With-

out you; _____ The joy and tears that love en-dears would have no

mean-ing, _____ If I did-n't have you _____ to keep me

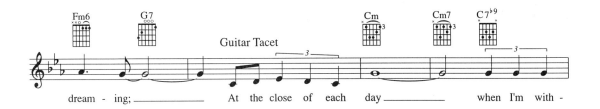

dream - ing; _____ At the close of each day _____ when I'm with -

out you, _____ And my heart kneels to pray, _____ I pray a -

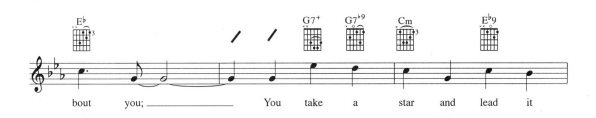

bout you; _____ You take a star and lead it

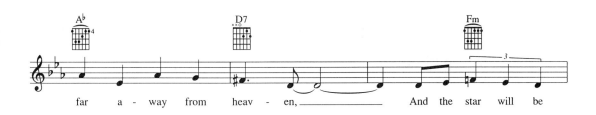

far a - way from heav - en, _____ And the star will be

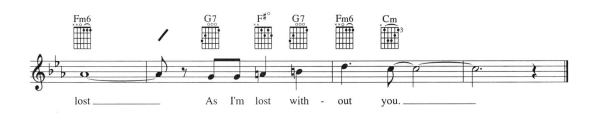

lost _____ As I'm lost with - out you. _____

31
Wonderful Illusion
(Uno)

Music by Marianito Mores & Enrique Santos Discepelo.
Words by Tommie Connor.

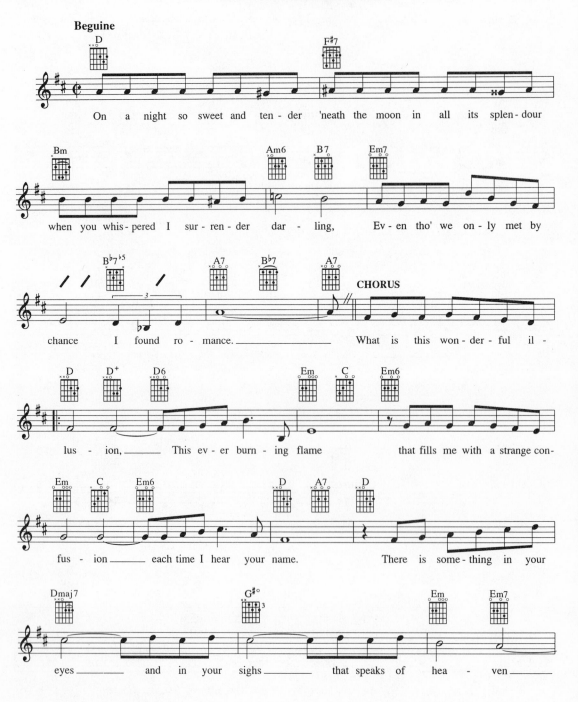

Beguine

On a night so sweet and ten-der 'neath the moon in all its splen-dour

when you whis-pered I sur-ren-der dar-ling, Ev-en tho' we on-ly met by

chance I found ro-mance._____ What is this won-der-ful il-

lus-ion,_____ This ev-er burn-ing flame that fills me with a strange con-

fus-ion_____ each time I hear your name. There is some-thing in your

eyes_____ and in your sighs_____ that speaks of hea-ven_____

32
You Belong To My Heart
(Solamente Una Vez)

English Lyric by Ray Gilbert.
Music & Spanish Words by Agustin Lara.

Beguine

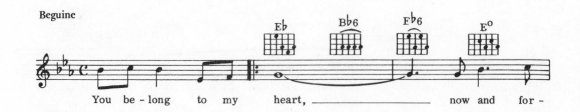

You be-long to my heart, _____ now and for-

ev - er, _____ And our love had it s start _____

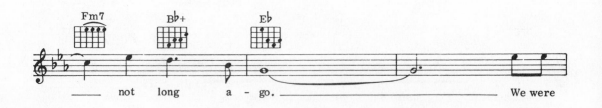

_____ not long a - go. _____ We were

gath - er - ing stars while a mil - lion gui-tars played our love song; _____

_____ When I said "I love you", ev-'ry beat of my heart said it

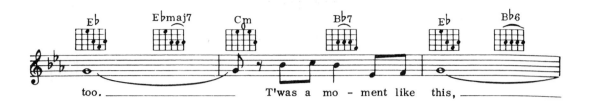

too. _____ T'was a mo - ment like this, _____

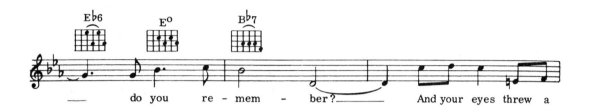

___ do you re - mem - ber? _____ And your eyes threw a

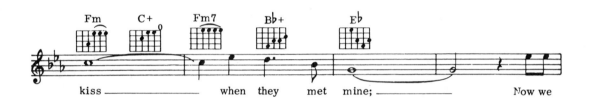

kiss _____ when they met mine; _____ Now we

own all the stars and a mil - lion gui-tars are still play - ing;

___ Dar-ling, you are the song and you'll al - ways be-long to my

heart. You be - long to my heart. _____

33
Volare

Words & Music by Domenico Modugno.
English Lyric by Mitchell Parish.

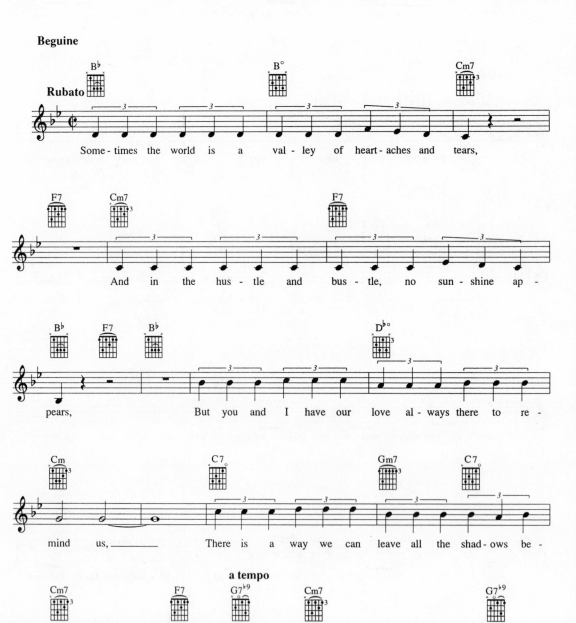

oh! _____ Can - ta - re, _____ oh, oh, oh, oh! _____ Let's

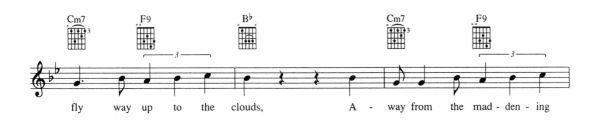

fly way up to the clouds, A - way from the mad - den - ing

crowds; We can sing in the glow of a star that I know of, Where

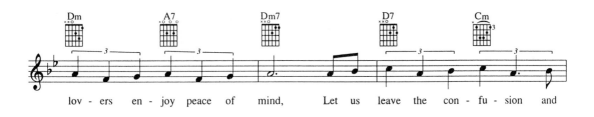

lov - ers en - joy peace of mind, Let us leave the con - fu - sion and

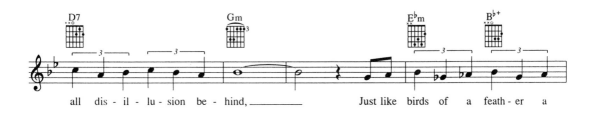

all dis - il - lu - sion be - hind, _____ Just like birds of a feath - er a

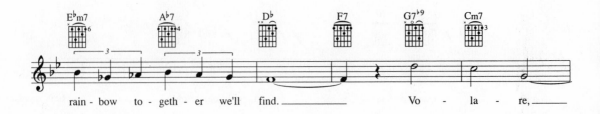

rain - bow to - geth - er we'll find._____ Vo - la - re,_____

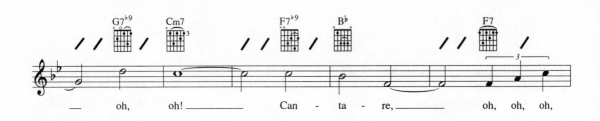

_ oh, oh!_____ Can - ta - re,_____ oh, oh, oh,

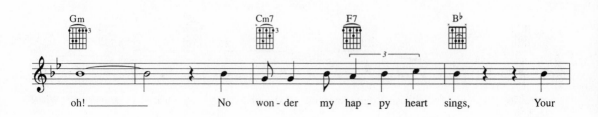

oh!_____ No won - der my hap - py heart sings, Your

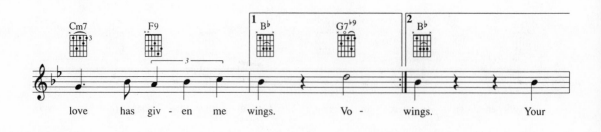

love has giv - en me wings. Vo - wings. Your

love has giv - en me wings Your love has giv - en me wings.

34
The Green Cockatoo

Words & Music by Don Rellegro.

treme - ly un - seem - ly to do. _____ But love came one day, in its

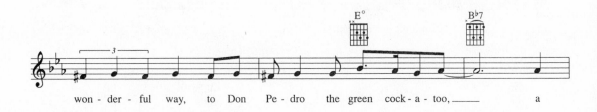

won - der - ful way, to Don Pe - dro the green cock - a - too, _____ a

young la - dy love bird, as sweet as a dove, heard the rep - ro - bate's hul - la - bal - oo. _

_____ With her wing she'd hid - den her head as she's bid - den in

"what a young love bird should do." _____ Don Pe - dro was smit - ten, with

love he was bit - ten, and start - ed that day _ to re - form. _____ Now

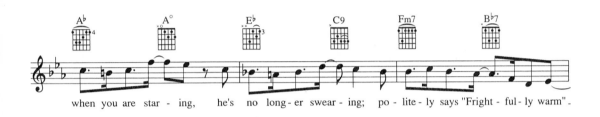

when you are star - ing, he's no long - er swear - ing; po - lite - ly says "Fright - ful - ly warm". _

_____ The rea - son is plain, _ but it's true, _____ He's re - cent - ly mur - mur'd "I do" _

_____ and now they're both hap - py, he'll soon be a "pap - py," Don

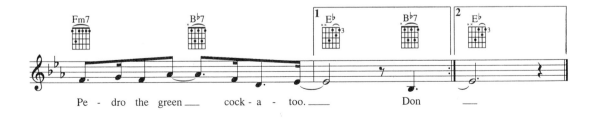

Pe - dro the green _ cock - a - too. _____ Don _____

35
Brazilian Summer

Original Words & Music by Caetano Zama.
English Lyrics by Michael Vaughan.

Samba

Some - where _____ a sum - mer night is fall - ing,

Some - where _____ a lone - ly voice is call - ing, "Come _____

_____ for I wait for you still, _____ In the heart of Bra - zil." _____

Those warm arms, _____ how tight they used to hold me,

Warm lips, _____ the love - ly things they told me, Oh, _____

_____ I re - mem - ber each thrill _____ of a sum - mer in old _____

_____ Bra - zil. _____ I see the stars on the

36
The Coffee Song

Words & Music by Bob Hilliard & Dick Miles.

Samba

Way down a-mong Bra-zil-ians cof-fee beans grow by the bil-lions, so they've got to find those ex-tra cups to fill, _____ _____ They've got an aw-ful lot of cof-fee in Bra-zil. _____ You can't get cher-ry so-da cause they've got to sell their quo-ta and the way things are I guess they nev-er will, _____ _____ They've got a zill-ion tons of cof-fee in Bra-zil.

37
Choo Choo Samba

Words by Jack Fishman.
Music by B.P. Godinho.

38
The Cactus Polka
(Jesusita En Chihuahua)

Original Words & Music by Edward H. Plumb.
English Lyric by Ervin Drake.

Samba

Soy muy fe - liz vi - si - tan - doê - sos lu - ga - res don - de
1. 'Neath south - ern stars down in Mex - i - co near Mag - da - le - na,
2. All thru the night when a cha - rro dan - cer's spurs are gleam - ing,

to - doês en - can - toŷ pla - cer y es - ven - tu - ra.
you'll hear gui - tars and the con - cert of a con - cert - i - na;
His eyes are bright and he kiss - es her 'til hers are beam - ing,

El e - xis - tir tie - ne me - nos - su - fri - mien - tos y los
grass full of scars, Danc - ing feet have made a gay a - re - na,
Camp - fire light makes a la - tin lov - er's heart go dream - ing

go - ces se su - ce - den con fre - cuen - ciaŷ bien es - tar.
Hey! A - mi - go! play as we go past in pol - ka time.
Hey! A - mi - go! play as we go past in pol - ka time.

Mi mo - re - na de ne - gros o - jos y bo - ca de - co - ral.
Dance, dance, dance in the cac - tus, dance in the cac - tus 'neath a mel - low moon!

39
Delicado

Composed by Waldyr Azevedo.

40
El Cumbanchero

English Lyric by Joe Crayhorn & George Williams.
Music by Rafael Hernandez.

1. El cum - ba, cum - ba, cum - ba, cum - ban -
   cum - ba, cum - ba, cum - ba, cum - ban -

- che - ro, In Span - ish means a rogue of a ran -
- che - ro, He's got a gal with plen - ty of di -

- che - ro, While the oth - er gauch - os work all day El
  ne - ro, He will tell her she's the on - ly one but

Cum - ban - che - ro spends his day at play,
when her back is turned just watch him run,

with a la - dy in his arms. _____ 2. El
to an - oth - er la - dy's arms. _____

Girls don't be - lieve that he _____ could tell a

41
Eso Beso

Words & Music by Joe & Noel Sherman.

Samba

Dm7 · G7 · Cmaj7

Es - o Bes - o! Ooh! That kiss!
sam - ba close like this!

Am7 · Dm7 · G7 · Cmaj7 · C7

Es - o Bes - o! Ooh! Your kiss! It's got
Ay! Ca - ram - ba, Need that kiss! Hold me

F · G · Em7⁻⁵ · A7 · 1. Em7

some - thing, Don't know what, But what - ev-er it's got,
clos - er, and we'll soar, For the

A7 · Dm7 · G7 (tacet - -) · 2. Dm7

it's got a lot! _____ When we sam - ba is the swing-in'-est

G9 · C · Fm7 · Bb7

way to make a - mor! As we dip and sway, and we ca-

42
(I Love You And)
Don't You Forget It

Words by Al Stillman.
Music by Henry Mancini.

43
Laughing Samba

Words by Benny Meroff & Anne Spear.
Music by Vincent Rizzo & George Johnson.

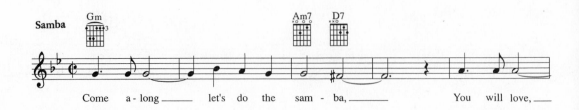

Come a-long ___ let's do the sam-ba, ___ You will love, ___

___ The laugh-ing sam-ba, ___ Pick your "chick" ___ and let's be-

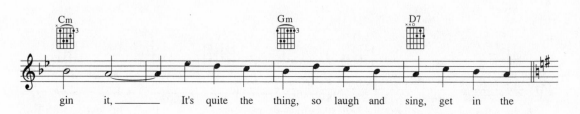

gin it, ___ It's quite the thing, so laugh and sing, get in the

swing. ___ Fun-ny lit-tle "song-a,"___

Some-thing like the con-ga, ___ It's the laugh-ing sam-ba, ___

Ha! Ha! Ha! Ha! Ha!   Ev - 'ry - one can do it, ___ There is noth - ing

to it, ___ Laugh your way right through it, ___ Ha! Ha! Ha! Ha! Ha!

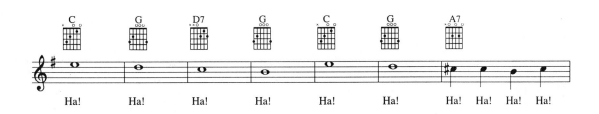

Ha!   Ha!   Ha!   Ha!   Ha!   Ha!   Ha! Ha! Ha! Ha!

Ha! (Hee! Hee! Hee!)   Goo - fy lit - tle "num - ba," ___ Sort - o like the

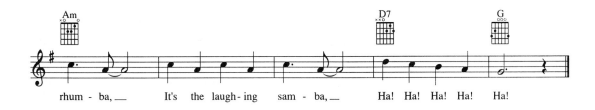

rhum - ba, ___ It's the laugh - ing sam - ba, ___ Ha! Ha! Ha! Ha! Ha!

44
Mambo Jambo
(Que Rico El Mambo)

Words by Raymond Karl & Charlie Towne.
Music by Perez Prado.

45
One Note Samba
(Samba De Uma Nota So)

Original Words by N. Mendonca.
English Lyric by Jon Hendricks. Music by Antonio Carlos Jobim.

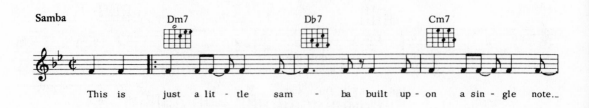

This is just a lit-tle sam-ba built up-on a sin-gle note.

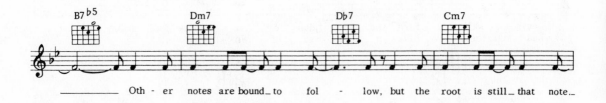

_____ Oth-er notes are bound_ to fol-low, but the root is still_ that note._

_____ Now this new one is_ the con-se-quence_ of the one we've just_ been through,

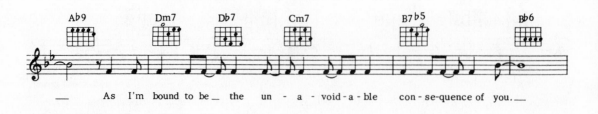

_ As I'm bound to be_ the un-a-void-a-ble con-se-quence of you._

There's so ma-ny peo-ple who can talk and talk and talk and just say no-thing,_ or near-ly

no - thing._ I have used up all the scale I know, and at the end I've come to

no - thing,_ or near-ly no - thing. So I come back to_ my first_

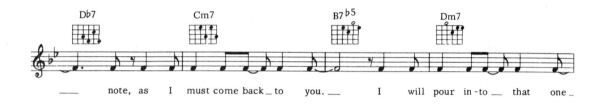

_ note, as I must come back_to you. _ I will pour in-to_ that one_

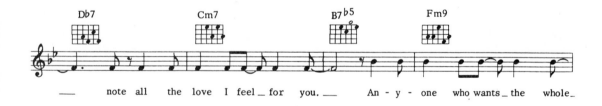

_ note all the love I feel_for you. _ An-y-one who wants_the whole_

_ show— Re Mi Fa Sol La_Ti Doh, _ He will find him-self_with no_

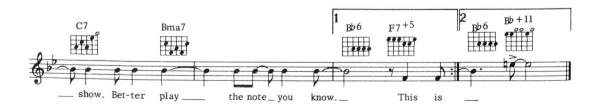

_ show. Bet-ter play ___ the note_ you know. _ This is __

46
The Peanut Vendor

Words by Marion Sunshine & L. Wolfe Gilbert.
Music by Moises Simons.

47
Quando, Quando, Quando

English Words by Pat Boone.
Italian Words by A. Testa. Music by Tony Renis.

48
The Three Caballeros

Music by Manuel Esperon.
Spanish Lyric by M. Cortazan. English Lyric by Ray Gilbert.

49
Tico Tico

Words by Ervin Drake.
Music by Zequinha Abreu.

50
The Wedding Samba

Words & Music by Abraham Ellstein, Allan Small & Joseph Liebowitz.

In old San - ta Fe When the stars are on — a hol - i - day
And they have killed the fat - ted cow, _____ Chi-
ci - ta and Ped - ro have brought a - bout _ this hol - i - day,
They're gon - na take the mar - riage vow. ___ And soon the band ___
_ will _ play a sam - ba, ___ That's on - ly played when - ev - er

51
Mañana
(Is Good Enough For Me)

Words & Music by Peggy Lee & Dave Barbour.

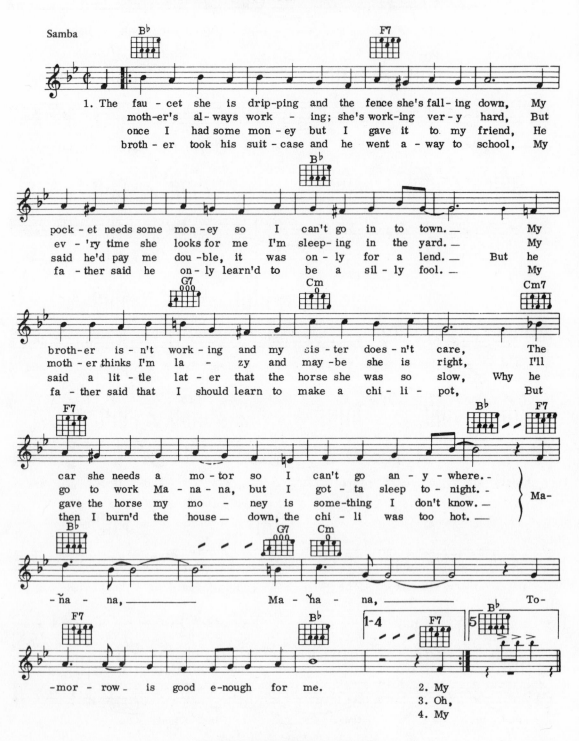

1. The fau-cet she is drip-ping and the fence she's fall-ing down, My
moth-er's al-ways work - ing; she's work-ing ver-y hard, But
once I had some mon-ey but I gave it to my friend, He
broth - er took his suit-case and he went a-way to school, My

pock - et needs some mon-ey so I can't go in to town. ___ My
ev - 'ry time she looks for me I'm sleep-ing in the yard. ___ My
said he'd pay me dou-ble, it was on-ly for a lend. ___ But he
fa - ther said he on-ly learn'd to be a sil-ly fool. ___ My

broth-er is - n't work-ing and my sis-ter does-n't care, The
moth - er thinks I'm la - zy and may-be she is right, I'll
said a lit-tle lat-er that the horse she was so slow, Why he
fa - ther said that I should learn to make a chi-li-pot, But

car she needs a mo-tor so I can't go an-y-where. _
go to work Ma-na-na, but I got-ta sleep to-night. _
gave the horse my mo - ney is some-thing I don't know. _
then I burn'd the house ___ down, the chi-li was too hot. ___

{ Ma-

-ña - na, _____ Ma - ña - na, _____ To-

1-4　　　**5**

-mor - row ___ is good e-nough for me.　　2. My
3. Oh,
4. My

52
No More Blues
(Chega De Saudade)

Original Words by Vinicius de Moraes.
English Words Jon Hendricks & Jessie Cavanaugh. Music by Antonio C. Jobim.

No more blues, I'm goin' back home, No, No more blues, I prom-ise no more to roam. Home is where the heart is. The fun-ny part is My heart's been right there all a-long.

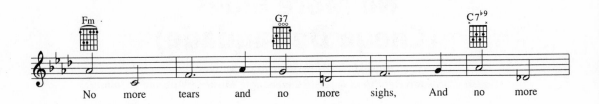

No more tears and no more sighs, And no more

fears, I'll say ___ no more ___ good-byes, ___ If trav-el beck-ons

me ___ I swear ___ I'm gon - na re-fuse, I'm gon - na

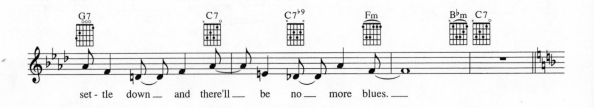

set - tle down ___ and there'll ___ be no ___ more blues. ___

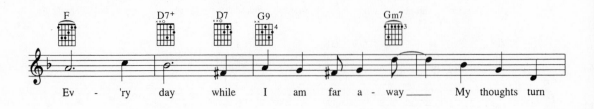

Ev - 'ry day while I am far a - way ___ My thoughts turn

home - ward, ___ for - ev - er home - ward, I trav - elled 'round the world ___

53
Agua De Beber
(Drinking Water)

Words by Norman Gimbel.
Music by Antonio Carlos Jobim.

2. The rain can fall on distant deserts,
   The rain can fall upon the sea,
   The rain can fall upon the flowers,
   Since the rain has to fall let it fall on me,
   Agua de beber, agua de beber camara
   Agua de beber, agua de beber camara.

3. I'll never see another Springtime,
   I'll never feel the summer sun,
   Unless you're there to share that Springtime,
   And like the rain and the flower our hearts are one,
   Agua de beber, give the flower water to drink
   Agua de beber, give the flower water to drink.

54
A Man And A Woman
(Un Homme Et Une Femme)

Original Words by Pierre Barouh.
English Lyric by Jerry Keller. Music by Francis Lai.

55
Cinnamon And Clove

Music by Johnny Mandel.
Words by Marilyn Bergman & Alan Bergman.

56
Felicidade

Words & Music by Antonio Carlos Jobim & Vinicius de Moraes.

57
The Gift
(Recado Bossa Nova)

Words & Music by Djalma Ferreira & Luiz Antonio.

58
The Girl From Ipanema
(Garota De Ipanema)

Original Words by Vinicius De Moraes.
English Lyric by Norman Gimbel. Music by Antonio Carlos Jobim.

59
Goodbye Sadness

Words & Music by Antonio Carlos Jobim & Vinicius de Moraes.

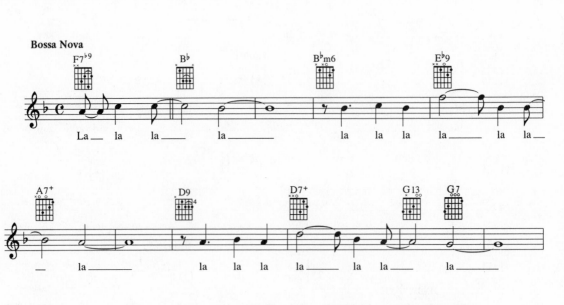

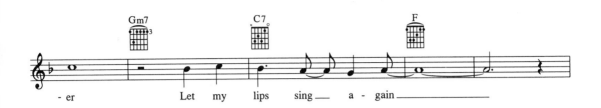

-er   Let my   lips sing __   a - gain _____

From   this   day   on   my days __ are days __   of sun __ and ros -

- es   My   nights a   car - ni - val __ of song _____

__   From   this   day   on, my dear, __ the   door __

__ to   sor - row clos -   es __   This   day   when

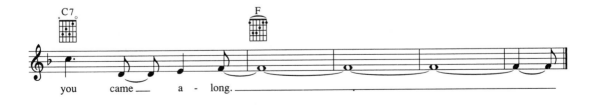

you came __ a - long. _____

60
How Insensitive

Music by Antonio Carlos Jobim.
Original Lyrics by Vinicius De Moraes. English Lyrics by Norman Gimbel.

61
Jazz 'N' Samba
(So Danco Samba)

Original Words & Music by Antonio Carlos Jobim & Vinicius de Moraes.
English Words by Norman Gimbel.

-stop U. S. A. _____ This new sound_____

came one day, ___ and it's clear that it's here to stay. _____ It's

jazz 'n' sam - ba, It's so re - fresh - ing. Like a new per - fume, ___

___ It's jazz 'n' sam - ba, It's jazz 'n' sam - ba

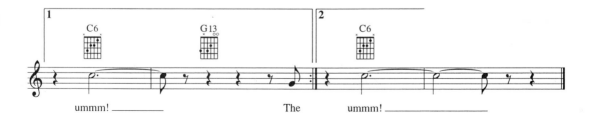

ummm! _____ The ummm! _____

62
Little Boat
(O Barquinho)

Music by Roberto Menescal.
Original Words by Ronaldo Boscoli. English Lyric by Buddy Kaye.

63
Meditation
(Meditacao)

Original Words by Newton Mendonca.
English Lyric by Norman Gimbel. Music by Antonio Carlos Jobim.

64
Quiet Nights Of Quiet Stars

English Words by Gene Lees.
Music & Original Words by Antonio Carlos Jobim.

65
Slightly Out Of Tune
(Desafinado)

English Lyric by Jon Hendricks & Jessie Cavanaugh.
Music by Antonio Carlos Jobim.

66
Song Of The Jet
(Samba Do Aviao)

Original Words & Music by Antonio Carlos Jobim.
English Words by Gene Lees.

67
Wave

Words & Music by Antonio Carlos Jobim.

68
Always In My Heart

Words by Kim Gannon.
Music by Ernesto Lecuona.

69
Ecstasy
(Extase Tango)

Words & Music by Jose Belmonte.

70
Jealousy

Words by Winifred May.
Music by Jacob Gade.

Jeal - ous-y! _____ 'twas on - ly through jeal - ous-y! _____

_____ Our hearts were bro - ken _____ and an - gry words were spo - ken. _____

_____ Now all I have is mem - o - ry _____ to che - rish so ten - der-ly,

_____ With ev - 'ry to - ken _____ you have gi - ven to me; _____

_____ I loved too well for I doubt - ed you in my

heart, My life was hell ev - 'ry mo - ment we were a-

- part, Why did I make that big mis-

71
Kiss Of Fire

Words & Music by Lester Allen & Robert Hill.

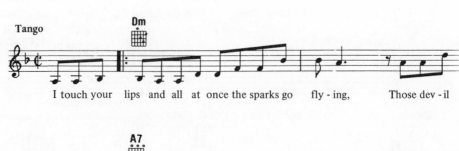

I touch your lips and all at once the sparks go fly-ing, Those dev-il

lips that know so well the art of ly-ing, And tho' I see the dan-ger, still the flame grows

high-er, I know I must sur-ren-der to your Kiss Of Fire.— Just like a

torch you set the soul with-in me burn-ing, I must go on a-long this road of no re-

turn-ing, And tho' it burns me and it turns me in-to ash-es, My whole world

crash-es with-out your Kiss Of Fire. I can't re-sist you, What good is there in

72
La Cumparsita

Music by Rodriguez.
English Lyric by Paco Liez.

Peo - ple call her

La Cum-par-si - ta, they will tell you there's no-one sweet - er,

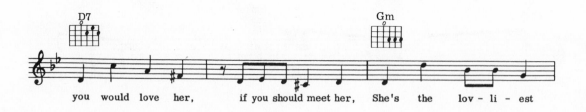

you would love her, if you should meet her, She's the lov - li - est

sen - or - i - ta. There is no - one who can com-pare with

73
Tell Me Marianne

English Adaptation by Bob Musel.
Music by Edgardo Donato.

Tan- gos set you dream- ing in a heav- en- ly trance,

South A- mer- i- can mag- ic did it bring you ro- mance?

Tell me why you're sigh- ing, has your fool- ish heart strayed?

For it seems you're al- ways list- 'ning to a dis- tant ser- en-

ade. Please tell me Mar- i- anne, why do you dream all day, Since you went on that

jour- ney down Ar- gen- ti- na way? Please tell me Mar- i- anne, who played the haunt- ing

tune that made your heart go danc- ing be- neath the Pam- pas moon? Was it

74
Hernando's Hideaway

Words & Music by Richard Adler & Jerry Ross.

way! O - lay! *(Instrumental)*

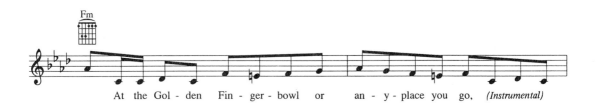

At the Gol - den Fin - ger - bowl or an - y - place you go, *(Instrumental)*

You will meet your Un - cle Max and

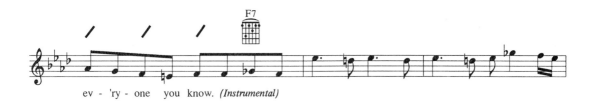

ev - 'ry - one you know. *(Instrumental)*

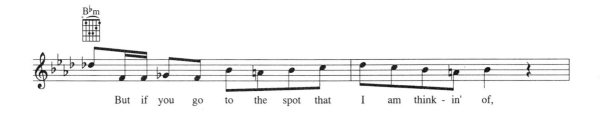

But if you go to the spot that I am think - in' of,

You will be free   to gaze at me   and talk of

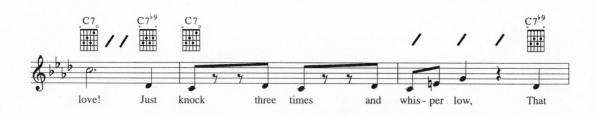

love!   Just   knock   three   times   and   whis-per   low,   That

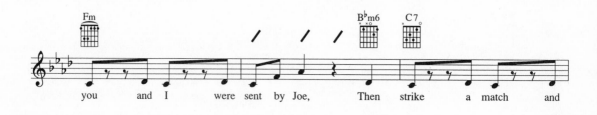

you   and   I   were sent by Joe,   Then   strike   a   match   and

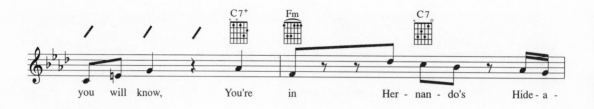

you   will know,   You're   in   Her - nan - do's   Hide - a -

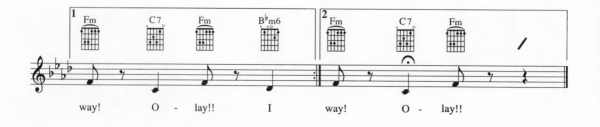

way!   O - lay!!   I   way!   O - lay!!

75
Torero

Words & Music by Renato Carosone, Nisa,
Al Hoffman & Dick Manning.

1. I met him on a bus in Bar - ce - lo - na, We
bragged a - bout the ma - ny se - ño - ri - tas, Who

kind - a got to talk - in', But he did all the
show - ered him with flow - ers, With big bou - quets of

talk - in'.＿＿＿ I asked him what he
flow - ers,＿＿＿ He told me that in

did in Bar - ce - lo - na, in sun - ny Bar - ce - lo - na, And
Hol - ly - wood, they want him to be like Mar - lon Bran - do, The

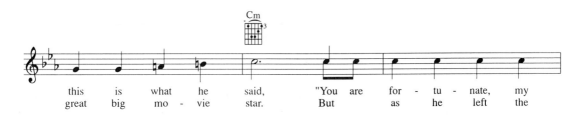

this is what he said, "You are for - tu - nate, my
great big mo - vie star. But as he left my the

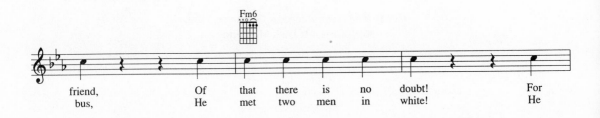

friend,   Of   that   there   is   no   doubt!   For
bus,   He   met   two   men   in   white!   He

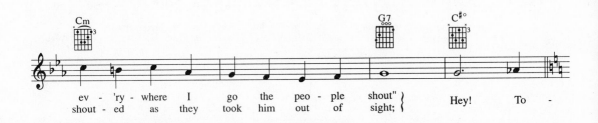

ev - 'ry - where I   go   the peo - ple   shout" }   Hey!   To -
shout - ed as they took him out of sight; }

Cha - cha - cha

re - ro, _____   Make way for Don Jo - sé, the great To -

Cha - cha - cha   *Cha - cha -*

re - ro, _____   In Spain I am a fa - mous ca - bal - le - ro. _____

cha

_____   I fight the bra - vest bull in all the land,   With a

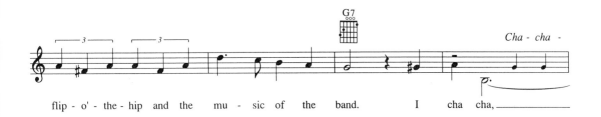

Cha - cha -

flip - o' - the - hip and the mu – sic of the band. I cha cha, _____

cha   *Cha - cha -*

_____ The bull is so con – fused, be - cause I cha cha, _____

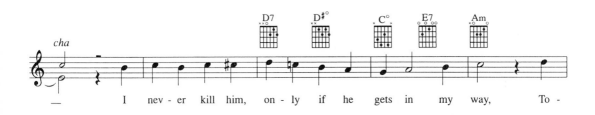

cha

_____ I nev - er kill him, on - ly if he gets in my way, To -

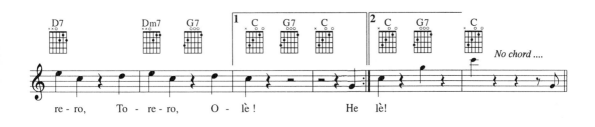

re - ro, To - re - ro, O - lè ! He lè!

No chord ....

O - lè!

76
Eso Es El Amor

Original Words & Music by Pepe Iglesias.
English Lyric by Sunny Skylar.

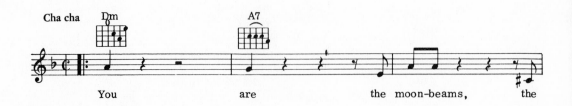

You are the moon-beams, the

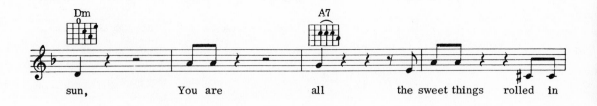

sun, You are all the sweet things rolled in

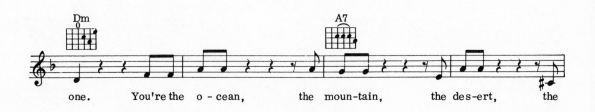

one. You're the o - cean, the moun-tain, the des-ert, the

foun-tain. You're sweet-ness and de - sire, the wa-ter and the

fire. E - so Es El A - mor. Si Se-

77
Farrago

By Barry White.

78
Never On Sunday

Words by Dilly Towns.
Music by Manos Hadjidakis.

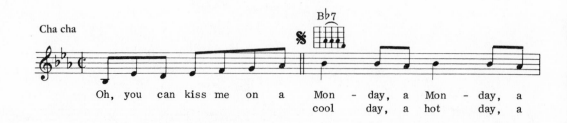

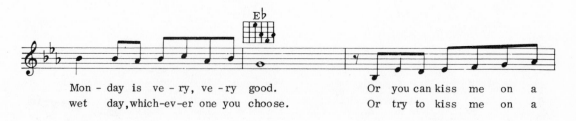

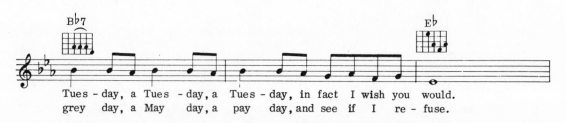

79
So Nice

Music & Original Lyrics by Marcos Valle & Paulo Sergio Valle.
English Lyrics by Norman Gimbel.

Cha cha

Some - one to hold me tight, that would be ve - ry nice,

Some-one to love me right, that would be ve - ry nice. Some-one to un-der-stand

each lit -tle dream__in me, Some-one to take my hand, to be a team__with me.

So nice, _____ life would be so nice, _____

____ If one day I'd find _____ some-one who would

take my hand and sam - ba thru' life _____ with me.

Some-one to cling to me, stay with me right _ or wrong, some-one to sing to me,

some lit -tle sam - ba song. Some-one to take my heart, then give his heart _ to me,

Some-one who's read-y to give love a start _ with me. Oh yes, _____

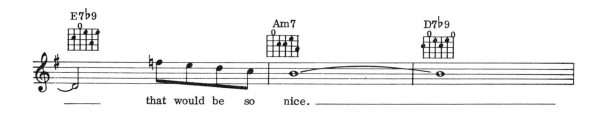

_____ that would be so nice. _____

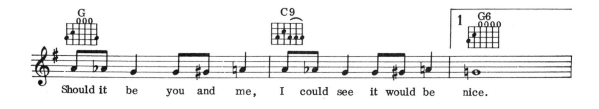

Should it be you and me, I could see it would be nice.

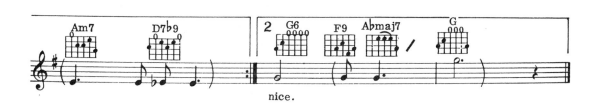

nice.

80
Wheels

Music by Norman Petty.

Cha cha

Wheels go round and that's how we be-gin it, This my friend is

love, And now you're in it! Wheels go round, A-round a mile a min-ute,

Fun-ny lit-tle Wheels in-side your heart. Till it's done, There'll

be no way o' know-in', Where you'll run or why you're all a-glow-in',

One by one they sim-ply get a-go-in', Wheels to spin the wheels that spin your

81
Besame Mucho

English Words by Sunny Skylar.
Music by Consuelo Velazquez.

Kiss me a - gain, ____ Kiss me my dar - ling; ____

Each time I cling to your kiss I hear mus-ic di - vine; ____

Bé - sa - me Mu - cho, ____

Hold me, my dar-ling and say that you'll al-ways be mine. ____

This joy is some-thing new, My arms en-fold-ing you, Nev-er knew this thrill be-

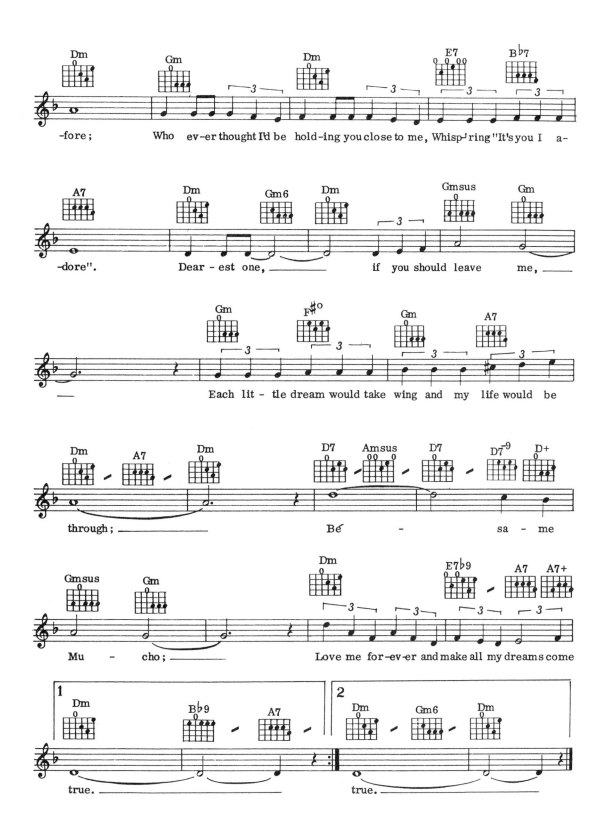

82
Frenesi

English Words by Ray Charles & S.K. Russell.
Music by Alberto Dominguez.

It was Fi-es-ta down in Mex-i-co,_____ And so I stopp'd a-while to

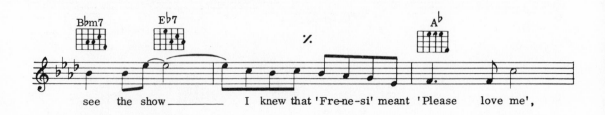

see the show_____ I knew that 'Fre-ne-si' meant 'Please love me',

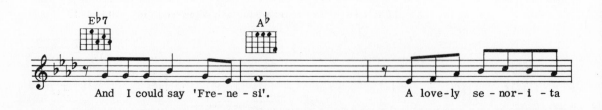

And I could say 'Fre-ne-si'. A love-ly se-nor-i-ta

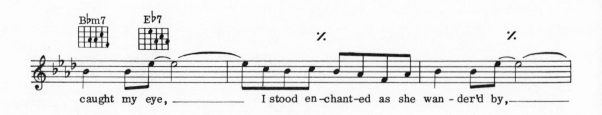

caught my eye,_____ I stood en-chant-ed as she wan-der'd by,_____

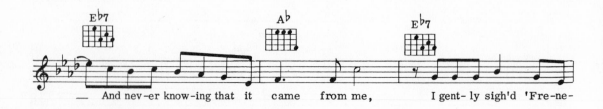

— And nev-er know-ing that it came from me, I gent-ly sigh'd 'Fre-ne-

83
Guantanamera

Words by Jose Marti.
Music Adaptation by Hector Angulo and Pete Seeger.

Guan-ta-na-me-ra   gua-ji - ra   Guan-ta-na-me-ra

Guan-ta-na-me - ra   gua-ji - ra   Guan-ta-na-me - ra!   ra!

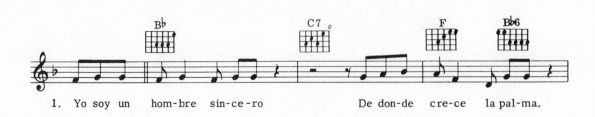

1. Yo soy un hom-bre sin-ce-ro   De don-de cre-ce la pal-ma.

Yo soy un hom-bre sin-ce-ro   De don-de cre - ce la

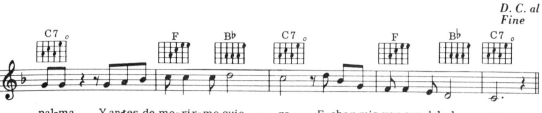

pal-ma.   Y an-tes de mo-rir-me quie - ro   E-char mis ver-sos del al - ma.

2. Mi verso es de un verde claro,
   Y de un carmin encendido.
   Mi verso es de un verde claro,
   Y de un carmin encendido.
   Mi verso es un cierro herido
   Que busca en el monte amparo.
   [Chorus]

3. Con los pobres de la tierra
   Quiero yo mi suerte echar.
   Con los pobres de la tierra
   Quiero yo mi suerte echar.
   El arroyo de la sierra
   Me complace mas que el mar.
   [Chorus]

Literal translation:

1. I am a truthful man from the land
   of palm trees.
   Before dying I want to share these
   poems of my soul.

2. My poems are light green,
   but they are also flaming crimson.
   My verses are like a wounded faun
   seeking refuge in the forest.

3. With the poor people of this earth
   I want to share my fate.
   The little streams of the mountains
   please me more than the sea.

84
La Cucaracha

Traditional.

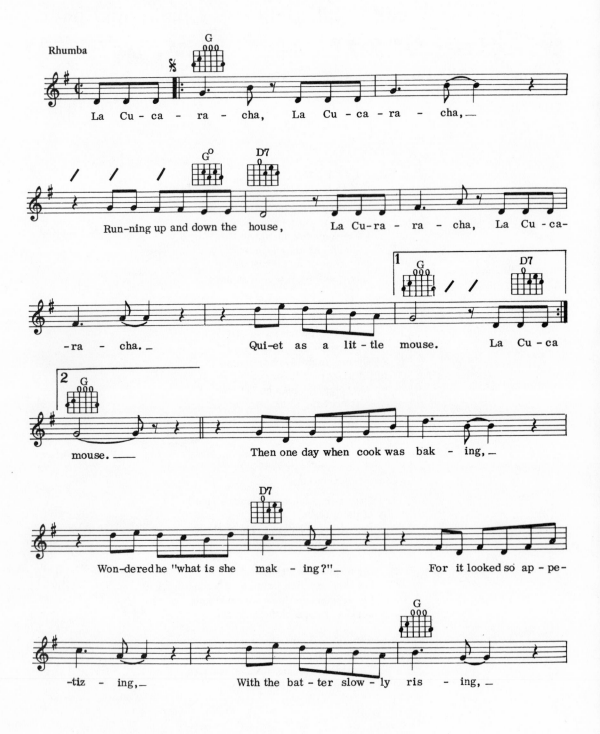

To the edge he start-ed skip - ping, — Then he found that he was

slip - ping, — In the pie so hot and blaz - in', —

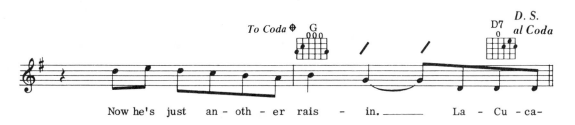

Now he's just an-oth-er rais - in. ———— La - Cu-ca-

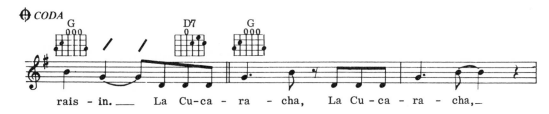

rais - in. —— La Cu-ca - ra - cha, La Cu-ca - ra - cha, —

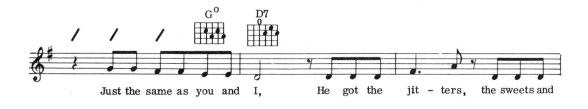

Just the same as you and I, He got the jit - ters, the sweets and

bit - ters, — Lived and loved and said "good-bye".

85
Baia
(Na Baixa Do Sapateiro)

Music by Ary Barroso.
English Lyric by Ray Gilbert.

Rhumba

Oh! _____ Ba - i - a - yah! _____ When twi - light is deep in the
Ai! _____ Qa - mô, ai, ai! _____ A - mô bo - ba - ge que a
Oi! _____ Ba - i - a ai, ai! _____ Ba - i - a que não me sa -

sky, ____ Ba - i - a - yah! _____ Some - one that I
gen - te não ex - pli - ca ai, ai! _____ Pro - va um bo - ca -
he do pen - sa - men - to, ai! _____ Fa - ço o meu la -

long to see __ Keeps haunt - ing my rev - er - ie, __ And so __ the
di - nho, oi! __ Fi - ca en - ve - na - do, oi! __ E pro res - to da
men - to, oi! __ Na de - ses - pe - ran - ça, oi! __ De en - con - trá prè - sse

lone - li - ness deep in my heart calls to you, calls to
vi - da é um tal de so - ffer, o la - rá, o le -
mun - do o a - mô que eu per - di na Ba - ia, vô con -

86
Kiss The Girl

Words by Howard Ashman.
Music by Alan Menken.

87
Make It Soon

Words & Music by Maurice Pon & Henri Salvador.
English Lyric by William Engvick.

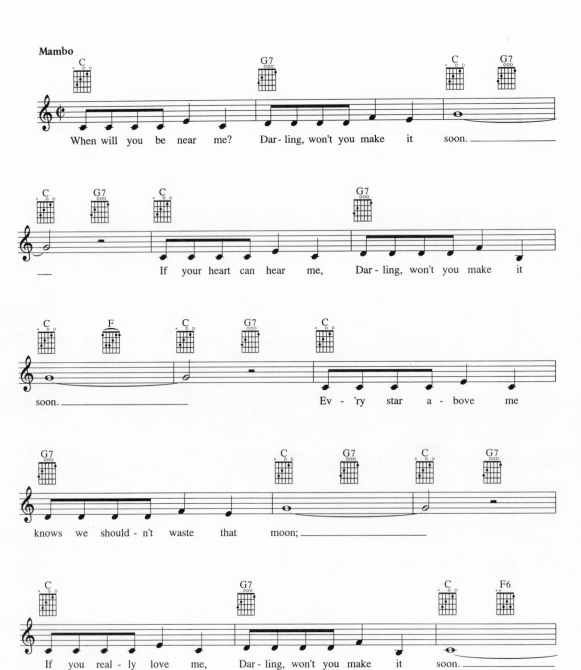

When will you be near me? Dar - ling, won't you make it soon. ___

___ If your heart can hear me, Dar - ling, won't you make it

soon. ___ Ev - 'ry star a - bove me

knows we should - n't waste that moon;

If you real - ly love me, Dar - ling, won't you make it soon.

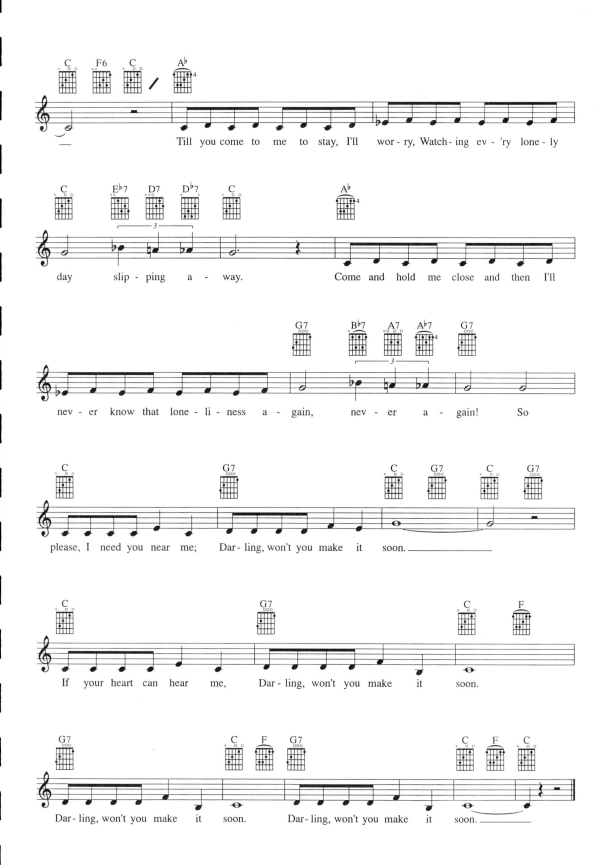

88
Mambo In The Moonlight

Words & Music by Buddy Kaye & Jules Loman.

Mambo

CHORUS

Mam - bo, mam - bo __ in the moon - light, __ In the moon - light __

it's a thrill! If the moon - light __ does - n't get __ { her, __ / him, __ }

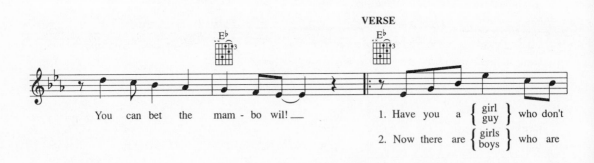

VERSE

You can bet the mam - bo wil! __ 1. Have you a { girl / guy } who don't

2. Now there are { girls / boys } who are

treat you nice, { Her / His } heart is just like a cake of ice,

ve - ry shy, They nev - er kiss but they'd like to try,

May - be { she's / he's } not the ro - man - tic kind, You can make { her / him }

Here is a new kind of re - ci - pe, And it works like

CHORUS

change { her / his } mind. — Just } mam - bo, mam - bo __ in the moon - light, __

T. N. T. __ Just }

In the moon - light __ it's a thrill! If the moon - light __

to 2nd verse

does - n't get __ { her, __ / him, __ } You can bet the mam - bo will! __

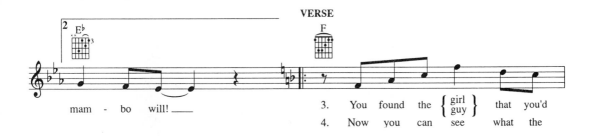

VERSE

mam - bo will! __

3. You found the { girl / guy } that you'd

4. Now you can see what the

like   to   wed,   But { she / he } wants some - bo - dy else in - stead,
mam - bo means,   Don't stay at home with your ma - ga - zines,

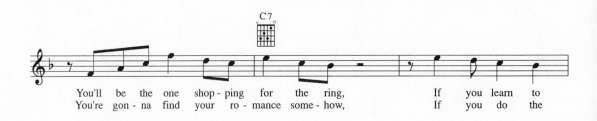

You'll be the one shop - ping for the ring,   If you learn to
You're gon - na find your ro - mance some - how,   If you do the

CHORUS

do one thing. __ Just } mam - bo, mam - bo ___ in the moon - light, __
mam - bo now. __ Just }

In the moon - light ___ it's a thrill!   If the moon - light __

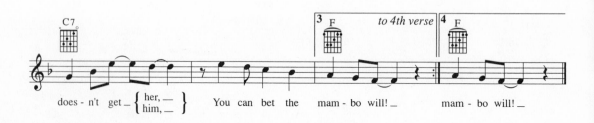

does - n't get _ { her, __ / him, __ } You can bet the mam - bo will! _ mam - bo will! _

89
Mambo Italiano

Words & Music by Bob Merrill.

Mambo

A girl went back to Na-po-li Be-cause she missed the

scen-er-y, The na-tive danc-es and the charm-ing songs, _____ But

wait a min-ute, some-thing's wrong 'Cause now it's Hey, mam-bo! Hey, mam-
Hey, mam-bo! Hey, mam-

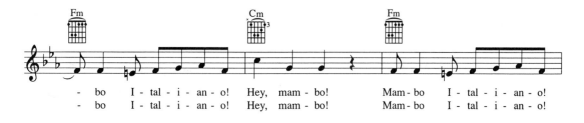

- bo I-tal-i-an-o! Hey, mam-bo! Mam-bo I-tal-i-an-o!
- bo I-tal-i-an-o! Hey, mam-bo! Mam-bo I-tal-i-an-o!

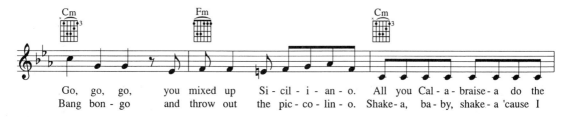

Go, go, go, you mixed up Si-cil-i-an-o. All you Cal-a-braise-a do the
Bang bon-go and throw out the pic-co-lin-o. Shake-a, ba-by, shake-a 'cause I

mam - bo like a cra - zy with a hey, mam - bo! Don't wan - na tar - an - tel - la,
love - a when you take - a me to hey, mam - bo! Down by the piz - zer - i - a,

Hey, mam - bo! No more - a moz - za - rel - la. Hey, mam - bo!
Ho, ho, ho, That's where I'm gon - na be - a. No, no, no,

Mam - bo I - tal - i - an - o! Try an en - cha - la - da with da fish - a - bac - a - lah and then a
Don't tell - a ma - ma mi - a. Ma - ma say "You stop - a or I'm gon - na tell - a pa - pa." And a

hey, goom - bah! _____ I love - a how you dance rhum - bah, _____
hey, ja - drool, _____ You don't - a have to go to school, _____

_ But take - a some ad - vice, pai - san - o, Learn - a how to mam - bo.
_ Just make - a wid da beat, bam bin - o, It's - a like a vin - o.

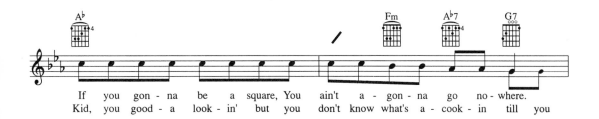

If   you gon - na   be   a   square, You   ain't   a - gon - na   go   no - where.
Kid, you good - a   look - in' but   you   don't know what's a - cook - in   till   you

Hey,   mam - bo!   Mam - bo   I - tal - i - an - o!   Hey,   mam - bo!
hey,   mam - bo!   Mam - bo   I - tal - i - an - o!   Hey,   mam - bo!

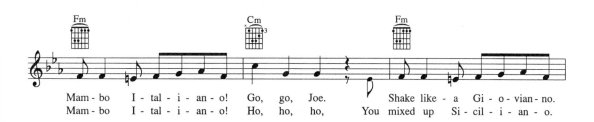

Mam - bo I - tal - i - an - o!   Go,   go,   Joe.   Shake like - a   Gi - o - vian - no.
Mam - bo I - tal - i - an - o!   Ho,   ho,   ho,   You mixed up   Si - cil - i - an - o.

Hel - lo, kess - e - deetch, You get - ta   hap - py   in   the feets a - when you mam - bo _____
It's - a   do de - lish - a   Ev - 'ry - bod - y come co - pish - a   how   to   mam - bo _____

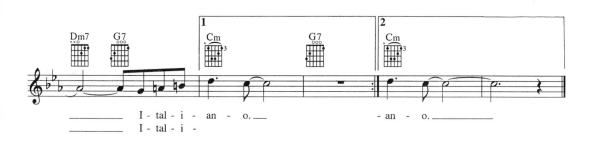

_____   I - tal - i - an - o. ___   - an - o. _____
_____   I - tal - i -

90
Anna

Music by V. Roman. Original Lyric by F. Giordano.
English Lyric by William Engvick.

There's a girl who the fel - las a - gree is a girl ev-'ry guy ought to

see. Take a look, take a look and you'll find that you can't get her out of your

mind. Who can say what it is that she's got, makes you think that it's spring when it's

not. Take a look, take a look and you'll say, "What a day! What a day! What a

day!" An - na's got that cer - tain some - thing that tops the

list, The kind of lips you'll nev - er re - sist, ____ They've got

____ to be kissed, ____ They've got ____ to be kissed, ____ right a -

91
Be True To Me
(Carnavalito)

Music by Edmundo P. Zaldivar.
English Lyric by George Thorn.

92
Cuanto Le Gusta

Words by Ray Gilbert.
Music by Gabriel Ruiz.

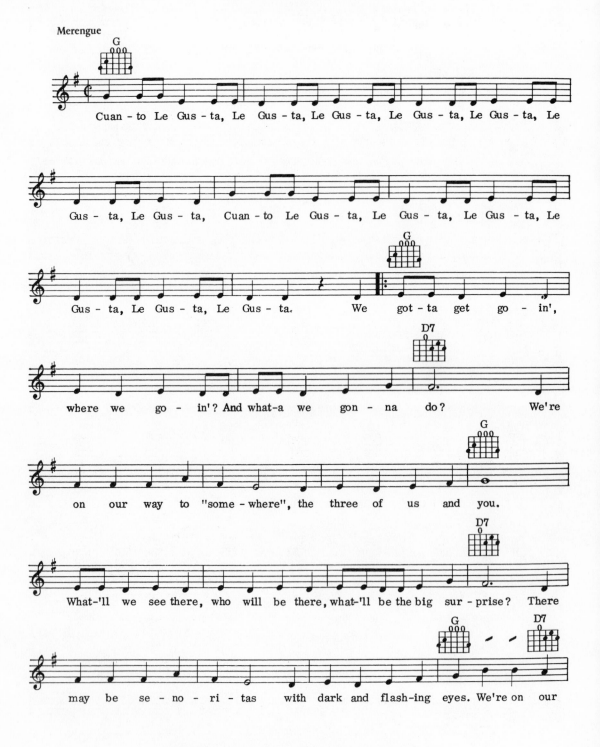

Merengue

Cuan - to Le Gus - ta, Le Gus - ta, Le Gus - ta, Le Gus - ta, Le Gus - ta, Le

Gus - ta, Le Gus - ta, Cuan - to Le Gus - ta, Le Gus - ta, Le Gus - ta, Le

Gus - ta, Le Gus - ta, Le Gus - ta. We got - ta get go - in',

where we go - in'? And what-a we gon - na do? We're

on our way to "some - where", the three of us and you.

What-'ll we see there, who will be there, what-'ll be the big sur - prise? There

may be se - no - ri - tas with dark and flash-ing eyes. We're on our

93
The Lonely Bull
(El Solo Toro)

By Sol Lake.

94
Malaguena

English Words by George Brown.
Music by Ernesto Lecuona.

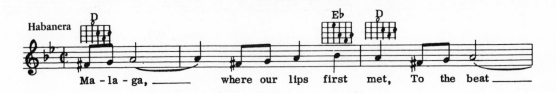

Ma - la - ga, _____ where our lips first met, To the beat _____

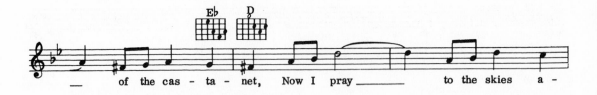

_ of the cas - ta - net, Now I pray _____ to the skies a -

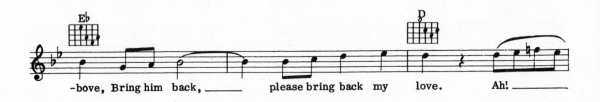

-bove, Bring him back, _____ please bring back my love. Ah! _____

_ Ma - la - ga, blue seas _ still

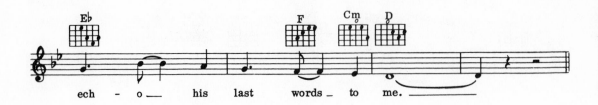

ech - o _ his last words _ to me. _____

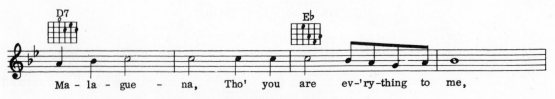

Ma - la - gue - na, Tho' you are ev - 'ry-thing to me,

95
Marianne

Words & Music by Terry Gilkyson, Frank Miller & Richard Dehr.

Calypso

CHORUS

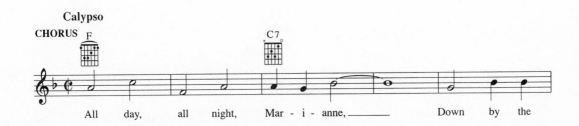

All day, all night, Mar - i - anne, _____ Down by the

sea - side sift - in' sand. _____ Ev - en lit - tle child - ren love

Mar - i - anne, _____ Down by the sea - side sift - in' sand. _____

VERSES

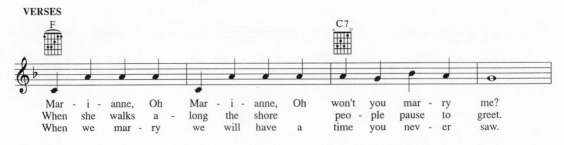

Mar - i - anne, Oh Mar - i - anne, Oh won't you mar - ry me?
When she walks a - long the shore peo - ple pause to greet.
When we mar - ry we will have a time you nev - er saw.

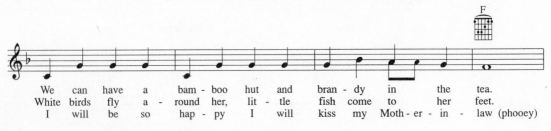

We can have a bam - boo hut and bran - dy in the tea.
White birds fly a - round her, lit - tle fish come to her feet.
I will be so hap - py I will kiss my Moth - er - in - law (phooey)

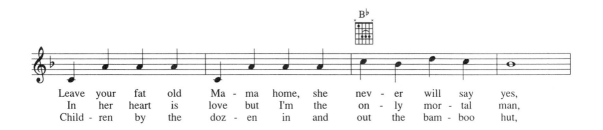

Leave your fat old Ma - ma home, she nev - er will say yes,
In her heart is love but I'm the on - ly mor - tal man,
Child - ren by the doz - en in and out the bam - boo hut,

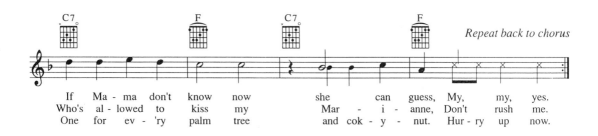

Repeat back to chorus

If Ma - ma don't know now she can guess, My, my, yes.
Who's al - lowed to kiss my Mar - i - anne, Don't rush me.
One for ev - 'ry palm tree and cok - y - nut. Hur - ry up now.

CHORUS *(After 3rd Verse)*

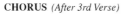

All day, all night, Mar - i - anne,_____ Down by the sea - side

sift - in' sand._____ Ev - en lit - tle child - ren love Mar - i - anne,_____

____ Down by the sea - side sift - in' sand._____

96
Take Her To Jamaica
(Where The Rum Come From)

Words by Jack Edwards.
Music by Irving Fields.

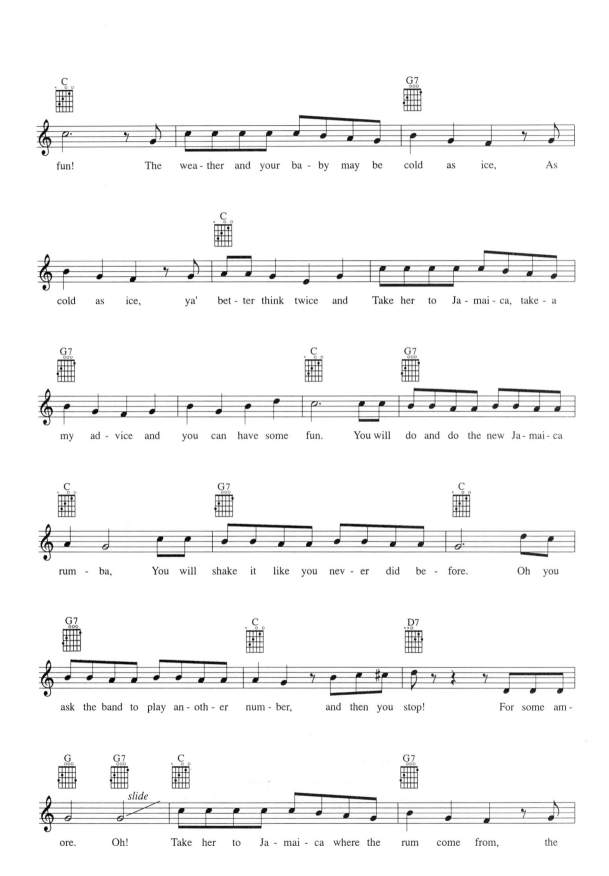

rum come from, the rum come from. Take her to Ja - mai - ca where the

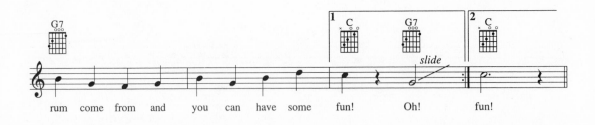

rum come from and you can have some fun! Oh! fun!

PATTER

To Patter

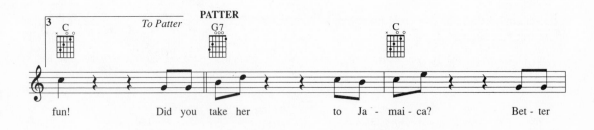

fun! Did you take her to Ja - mai - ca? Bet - ter

take her to Ja - mai - ca. Gon - na take her to Ja -

mai - ca? Then do it, do it, do it right a - way o - ley.

97
Love Me With All Your Heart
(Cuando Calienta El Sol)

Music by Carlos Rigual & Carlos A. Martinoli.
Original Words by Mario Rigual. English Lyric by Michael Vaughn.

Slow Latin Rock

Love me with all your heart, __ that's all I want, love; __

Love me with all of your heart, or not at all; Just pro-mise me this: __ that you'll

give me __ all your kiss-es, __ Ev-'ry win-ter, __ ev-'ry sum-mer, __ ev-'ry fall.

When we are far a-part, __ or when you're near me, __ Love me with all of your heart, as I love

you; Don't give me your love __ for a mo-ment, __ or an hou- r, __ Love me

al-ways, __ as you lov'd me __ from the start With ev-'ry beat of your heart. __ (Instrumental)

98
Vaya Con Dios

Words & Music by Larry Russell, Inez James & Buddy Pepper.

99
Brazilian Love Song

Words by Nat Cole, Dick Manning, Al Hoffman.
Music by Breno Ferreira.

I see a lit-tle bird that is sit-tin' in the tree-top, A pret-ty lit-tle

bird that is sit-tin' in the tree-top, I see a lit-tle bird that is sit-tin' in the

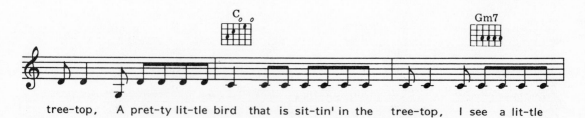

tree-top, A pret-ty lit-tle bird that is sit-tin' in the tree-top, I see a lit-tle

bird that is sit-tin' in the tree-top, A pret-ty lit-tle bird that is sit-tin' in the

tree-top, I see a lit-tle bird that is sit-tin' in the tree-top, A pret-ty lit-tle

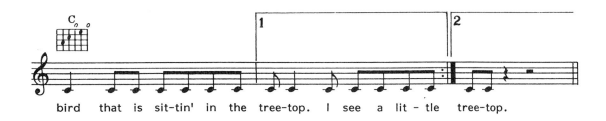

bird that is sit-tin' in the tree-top. I see a lit - tle tree-top.

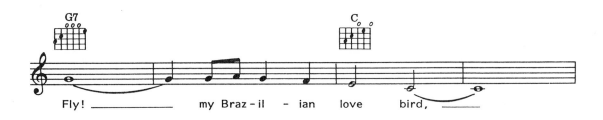

Fly! _____ my Braz-il – ian love bird, _____

Fly! _____ to the one I love, _____

Please _____ won't you tell her that I'm the one who cares,

Please _____ bring to me her ans - wer. _____

100
I Came, I Saw, I Conga'd

Words & Music by James Cavanaugh, John Redmond & Frank Weldon.

_ adds so mu - cha _____ to your charms. _____

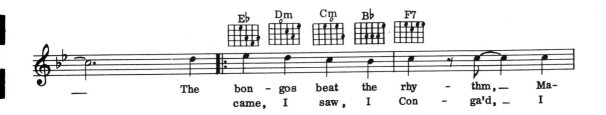

_ The bon - gos beat the rhy - thm, _ Ma-
came, I saw, I Con - ga'd, _ I

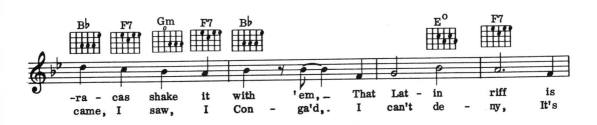

-ra - cas shake it with 'em, _ That Lat - in riff is
came, I saw, I Con - ga'd, . I can't de - ny, It's

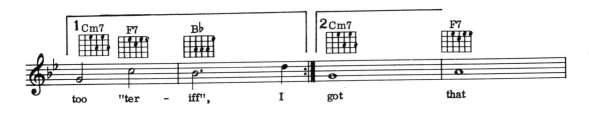

too "ter - iff", I got that

I, yi, Con - ga, _ I, yi, Con - ga, _

I, yi, Con - ga, _ Yi.

101
Maria Elena

Music by Lorenzo Barcelata.
English Lyric by S.K. Russell.

Waltz moderato

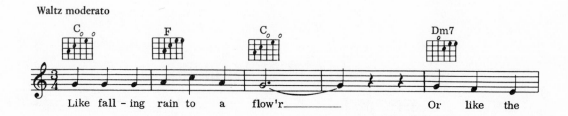

Like fall-ing rain to a flow'r___ Or like the

shore to the sea,___ Like min-utes are to an

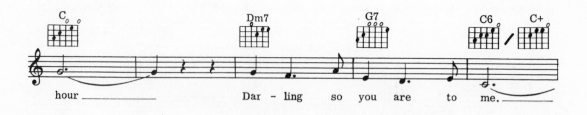

hour___ Dar-ling so you are to me.___

This I can nev-er dis-guise___

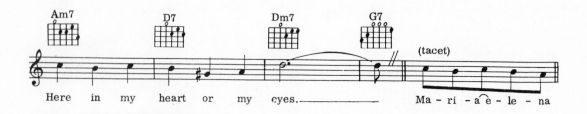

Here in my heart or my eyes.___ (tacet) Ma-ri-a e-le-na

Plus many indispensable collections of special interest:
101 Jazz & Blues Hits ...
101 Showtunes ...
101 Beatles Songs ...
101 Pub Favourites ...
and more.

Busking For Special Occasions 101 Songs:
Piano/Organ/Guitar
AM29596

101 Rock'n'Roll Hits for Buskers
Piano/Organ/Guitar
AM36484

101 Pub Favourites for Buskers
Piano/Organ/Guitar
AM62761

101 Christmas Hits for Buskers
Piano/Organ/Guitar
AM64569

101 Australian Songs For Buskers
Piano/Organ/Guitar
AM68073

101 Beatles Songs for Buskers
Piano/Organ/Guitar
N018392

101 Country Hits for Buskers
Piano/Organ/Guitar
AM33580

101 Jazz & Blues Hits for Buskers
Piano/Organ/Guitar
AM60245

101 Stage & Screen Hits For Buskers
Piano/Organ/Guitar
AM72612

101 Folk Songs for Buskers
Piano/Organ/Guitar
AM69220

101 Comedy Hits for Buskers
Piano/Organ/Guitar
AM37912

101 Australian Songs For Buskers, Book 2
Piano/Keyboard/Guitar
AM78684

101 Children's Songs For Buskers
Piano/Organ/Guitar
AM74584

101 Showtunes For Buskers
Piano/Organ/Guitar
AM32509

101 Classical Themes For Buskers
Piano/Organ/Guitar
AM65319

101 Pop Hits for Buskers
Piano/Organ/Guitar
AM61763

101 Rock Hits for Buskers
AM65806

101 Rock Hits for Buskers, Book 2
AM84716

New from Music Sales - the one-and only, ultimate busker book! It's *the* book to take to a party... to a gig... on your holiday... or to that famous desert island!

It's packed with literally hundreds and hundreds of the best-loved songs of all time... from vintage standards of the 30s right through to the latest pop hits.

"Probably the best songbook in the world."

The Busker's Fake Book
1001 All-Time Hit Songs

"The only songbook you'll ever need!"

"The Suitcase Book"!

For piano, organ, guitar, all electronic keyboards and all 'C' instruments. With an easy-to-use A-Z title finder plus a classified 'song type' index. As a taster, here's just a quarter of the titles in this unique bumper songbook...

'A' You're Adorable	Hello, Goodbye	Ruby Don't Take Your Love To Town
A Fine Romance	Here, There And Everywhere	Satin Doll
A Fool Such As I	Hey Jude	Scarborough Fair
A Hard Day's Night	Hey, Good Lookin'	Shake Rattle And Roll
A Man And A Woman	Honeysuckle Rose	She Loves You
A Teenager In Love	I Came I Saw I Conga'd	Singing The Blues
Act Naturally	I Don't Want To Spoil The Party	Sixteen Tons
Against All Odds	I Dreamed A Dream	Sloop John B
Ain't Misbehavin'	I Feel Pretty	Smoke Gets In Your Eyes
All I Have To Do Is Dream	I Fought The Law	Solitude
All My Loving	I Left My Heart In San Francisco	Something
America	I Saw Her Standing There	Somewhere
An American In Paris	I'm A Loser	Spanish Eyes
An Old Fashioned Love Song	I'm Beginning To See The Light	Standing On The Corner
Angel Eyes	I'm Still Standing	Stars Fell On Alabama
Another Suitcase In Another Hall	If I Had A Hammer	Stranger In Paradise
As Time Goes By	If I Were A Bell	Strangers In The Night
Band On The Run	In The Air Tonight	Streets Of London
Barbara Ann	It Never Rains In Southern California	Sugarbush
Baubles Bangles And Beads	It's Not Unusual	Sultans Of Swing
Because	It's So Easy	Summertime Blues
Bennie And The Jets	Jambalaya	Sunshine Of Your Love
Big Girls Don't Cry	Jealous Guy	Sweet Charity
Big Spender	La Ronde De l'Amour	Swing Low, Sweet Chariot
Bird Dog	Lady D'Arbanville	Take Back Your Mink
Blowin' In The Wind	The Lady In Red	Take That Look Off Your Face
Boogie Woogie Bugle Boy	The Lambeth Walk	Take The 'A' Train
Buffalo Gals	The Last Time I Saw Paris	Teen Angel
Bye Bye Love	Layla	The Tender Trap
California Dreaming	Leaning On A Lamp Post	That'll Be The Day
Can't Smile Without You	Let It Be	Theme For A Dream
Candle In The Wind	Let's Twist Again	These Foolish Things
Caravan	The Lion Sleeps Tonight	They Didn't Believe Me
Chantilly Lace	Live And Let Die	This Guy's In Love With You
Come Fly With Me	Long Tall Sally	This Land Is Your Land
Consider Yourself	Love And Marriage	Those Were The Days
Crazy	Lover Man	Three Little Fishies
Cruising Down The River	Lucille	Till There Was You
Dancing Queen	Lick Be A Lady	To Know Him Is To Love Him
Daniel	Lullaby Of Birdland	Tonight
Desafinado	Maple Leaf Rag	True Love Ways
Devil In Disguise	Mario	Tulips From Amsterdam
Diamonds Are A Girl's Best Friend	Me And My Girl	Tutti Frutti
Do You Know The Way To San Jose	Mister Bojangles	Unchained Melody
Don't Cry For Me Argentina	Money For Nothing	Under The Boardwalk
Don't Pay The Ferryman	Mull Of Kintyre	Up, Up And Away
Don't Sleep In The Subway	Never On A Sunday	Uptown Girl
Eastenders	Nights In White Satin	The Very Thought Of You
Ebony And Ivory	Norwegian Wood	Wake Up Little Susie
Eleanor Rigby	Not Fade Away	Walk Tall
Empty Chairs At Empty Tables	O Sole Mio	The Way You Look Tonight
The Entertainer	Oh Pretty Woman	We Can Work It Out
Every Breath You Take	Ol' Man River	We Don't Need Another Hero
First Time Ever I Saw Your Face	Old Shep	We Shall Overcome
Fools Rush In	On A Slow Boat To China	We'll Meet Again
From Me To You	Only The Lonely	What Kind Of Fool Am I
Funiculi, Funicula	P.S. I Love You	Wheels
Für Elise	Peggy Sue	When I'm Sixty Four
Get Back	Pennies From Heaven	When Irish Eyes Are Smiling
Get It On (Bang A Gong)	Penny Lane	When This Lousy War Is Over
The Girl From Ipanema	Pigalle	Where Have All The Flowers Gone
Good Vibrations	Poison Ivy	Witchcraft
Goodbye Yellow Brick Road	The Power Of Love	With A Little Help From My Friends
Guys And Dolls	Raindrops Keep Falling On My Head	Woman
Happy Xmas (War Is Over)	Rave On	Yellow Submarine
Hava Nagilah	Rhapsody In Blue	Yesterday
He Ain't Heavy He's My Brother	Riders On The Storm	Your Cheatin' Heart
Hello Mary Lou	Rock Around The Clock	Your Song

Melody, lyrics and guitar chords to literally hundreds and hundreds of the best songs of all time... from the golden standards through to the great pop hits of today.

*Wise Publications
Order No. AM9xxxx*

While compiling this huge book, editor/arranger Peter Lavender kept all the artwork in a huge suitcase! But now that it's printed, this new mega-bumper busker book is a lot easier to carry around!

Surprisingly portable, in fact, at the usual songbook size of 12" x 9"... with some 656 pages!

As well as the 1,001 songs, the book includes a handy A-Z alphabetical title index *and* a classified index, too.